Little Miss Geek

Bridging The Gap Between Girls And Technology

Belinda Parmar

Little Miss Geek
Bridging The Gap Between Girls And Technology

Written by: Belinda Parmar

Lady Geek Ltd
www.ladygeek.com

@LadyGeekTV
LadyGeekTV

ISBN: 978-0-9573898-0-9

Lady Geek

Little Miss Geek

Bridging The Gap Between Girls And Technology

Belinda Parmar

Contents

Foreword

MARTHA LANE FOX
UK'S DIGITAL CHAMPION

The timing of Little Miss Geek couldn't be better. We live in an age when 'digital' is as vital and basic a life skill as knowing how to read and write. Digital skills are now essential for education and employment: we know that you're 25% more likely to get work when you have web skills and, once in that job, you'll earn 10% more.

The Internet makes a staggering difference in people's lives, but women are under-represented as both consumers and creators of Internet technology. In business, nearly half of our largest 250 companies have no women in their boardrooms. And in technology, a sector that was 22% female 10 years ago, there is a workforce that is now just 17% female and declining.[1] I believe change is needed: technology has to become a career that welcomes the next generation of talented young women.

We have to shatter the perception that people who work in I.T. are sad, eccentric, pizza guzzling nerds. Our girls must be inspired to become equal players amongst the next generation of inventors and technology leaders.

I want to live in a world that reflects our population. I want women's opinions to inform how technology products are designed and marketed. I want more women starting businesses, going into science, taking equal share of power, wealth and influence. I want women to have a bigger voice.

This book is the start of a campaign that aims to change the dynamics of the country by bridging the gap from women as consumers of technology to women as creators of technology. Little Miss Geek is a wake-up call for technology business leaders. This book will help companies attract, motivate and retain women. This book also provides practical solutions to recruit from a wider talent pool and inspire the next generation of young female inventors, developers and designers.

Technology should not be exclusively a world of men and boys. Our technology gurus and heroes cannot be limited to men. It's a digital world now and the digital world is for everyone. Don't let anyone tell you otherwise.

• •

Martha Lane Fox, UK Digital Champion and Chair of Go ON UK. She also Co-Founded Lastminute.com and LuckyVoice and sits on the boards of M&S and MyDeco.com.

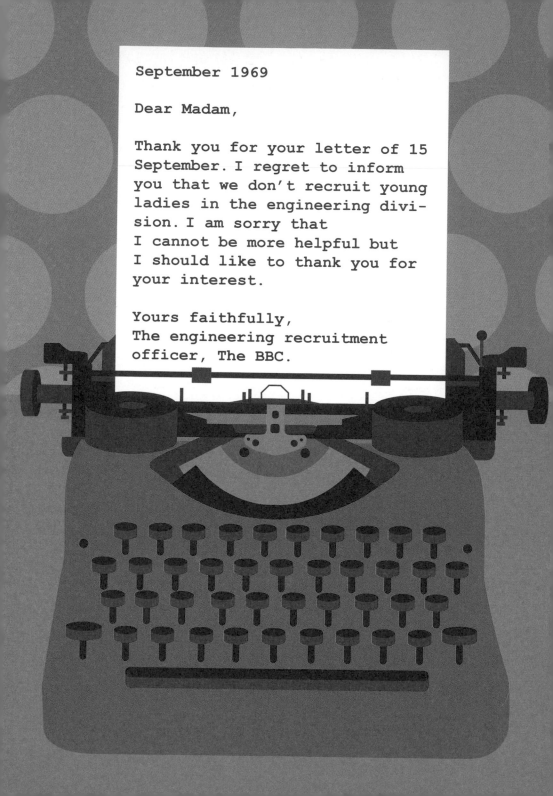

Preface

As I walk down the aisle I'm accosted by a young man wearing the uniform of one of the UK's better-known electronic retailers. His voice hits just the right balance between patronising and surly. 'You alright there, love?' I almost instantly regret telling him that I'm shopping for a new laptop. He starts gesturing frantically at a shelf full of low-end, brightly-coloured models while reeling off stats as if everyday English had suddenly given way to a code made-up of numbers and acronyms.

As I watch him I can't help but detect the pity and irritation in his expression. His mouth says 'I'm here to help' but his eyes say 'I think perhaps I'd better talk to your husband instead.' Sadly for him my husband isn't with me. I've worked in the tech industry for over fifteen years – on advertising and marketing big brands such as IBM, HP, Vodafone, Nokia, Xbox and Microsoft. I know what I want and I can make my own mind up. And yet his supercilious droning is starting to make me feel like a child on the first day of school being bullied by the snotty prefect for not knowing where the toilets are.

But this is a double-edged sword, because for every tech retailer or product marketer who thinks women won't touch a netbook unless it's the colour of Carrie Bradshaw's favourite cupcake, there are a dozen smart, tech-literate, creative female professionals who wouldn't dream of applying for a job (and much less a career) in a sector perceived as grey, dull and uninspiring. Women's rejection of the tech sector is every bit as damaging as the sector's condescending attitude towards female consumers. I would argue that very little has changed since 1969 when this BBC rejection letter was received (see page 8).

Only 17% of the technology workforce in this country is female,[1] and yet women buy 40% of all technology products.[2] Only 4% of all games developers are female[3] despite women now playing 55% of all 'casual' games.[4]

At heart this is a question of frozen attitudes. Women spend more and more money on tech products which have become increasingly important parts of their everyday lives, and yet a rift still exists between women and the tech industry. The former regard the entire sector as populated by stultifying geeks, while the latter regards the former as undiscerning secondary consumers. A mere afterthought in design and marketing strategies.

The situation is crying out for change. We need to change the technology and games industry from the inside out. We need to make tech companies a better place for women to work and flourish. And we need to make women aware of this shift, because until more women start to take up creative, innovative and pioneering roles within the industry, the products that emerge are going to continue to pander to the perceived interests of the core male consumer base.

We need to inspire the next generation of female talent to want to be part of this industry. My vision for this book is to inspire girls to become *creators* of technology as well as *consumers*. I want it to start to bridge the gap.

Computer games now account for greater revenue than film, and have every bit as much impact on today's generation of children growing up as the movie stars of the past did on the adults of today. *And yet what young girl would put a career as a games designer above that of a Hollywood director?*

Call it what you like: cachet; image; prestige; glamour, Hollywood has it in spades, while nothing even remotely associated with tech inspires more than a glazed look in the average teen.

This needs to change, because as much as the current tablets, smartphones and games define our present, so the innovations waiting round the corner will define our future. That is the stuff of dreams and aspirations, and I want girls all around the world to dream of creating things that change *people's* lives. *Their* lives. *Our* lives.

I need your help in changing things. Please do get in touch if you want to be part of this campaign.

There are a great many without whom this book wouldn't have been possible. So (deep breath), my thanks go out to Dan Whitcombe (my talented oldest friend, writer and proofreader), to James Fritz for his genius input and ideas, to James Barker for his weird and wonderful illustrations, to Lucie Sarif for her creative ideas and commitment to our vision, to Chris Timoney for his visual flair and amazing infographics, to my husband Sal for many long, boring nights going over drafts, to Caroline Hooper for never once letting me down (and her invaluable big red pen), and finally to Joana Pereira, for being an incredible designer (and never giving up) and for somehow putting (and keeping) all this together.

But now I need introduce you to the star of the show, *Little Miss Geek…*

Belinda

@belindaparmar,
CEO of Lady Geek.

Brilliant Companies In This Space:

BCS WOMEN, **CATALYST,** CISCO, E-SKILLS UK, **EWIN BY eBAY,** FINDING ADA, GAMES BRITANNIA, **COMPUTING AT SCHOOL,** DWEN BY DELL, INTELLECT, THE UKRC, **GIRLS IN TECH,** GIRLS WHO CODE, **GEEK GIRL MEETUP,** PINKSTINKS, GIRLS 'N' GADGETS, **LADIES WHO CODE,** GIRLYGEEKDOM, MUMPRENEUR UK, **WOMEN IN GAMES,** REWIRED STATE & YOUNG REWIRED STATE, THE NATIONAL CENTER FOR WOMEN AND INFORMATION TECHNOLOGY, THE NEXT WOMEN, WOMEN IN TECHNOLOGY, **WOMAN'S HOUR (BBC RADIO 4),** NOKIA'S REMARKABLE WOMEN CAMPAIGN, ROOMINATE, **MzTEK** AND VODAFONE mWOMEN.

Acknowledgments

I would like to give special thanks to the following people.
Without their support, this book would not have been possible

DAME WENDY HALL, SHOSHI ROBERTS, MAGGIE BERRY,
MARTHA LANE FOX, MAGGIE PHILBIN, BECCA CADDY,
EMMA MULQUEENY, SAMANTHA BAIL, MAZZ MOSLEY,
EMMA VANSTONE, KATE CRAIG-WOOD, LAURA DIXON,
MARK HARDISTY, IAN LIVINGSTONE, EMER COLEMAN,
KERRY FARROW, DR. JUDY ROBERTSON, DR. JO TWIST,
EMMA MOORE, DR. TOM CRICK, ANN CHARLES,
NATASHA ROONEY, DAVID BRABEN, CLAIRE VYVYAN,
LEE EPTING, DR. JACKIE GRANLEESE, KATIE LEE,

JULIE MEYER, DR. TRACY CAMP, DR. KAREN TREW,
KEZA MACDONALD, MEAGHAN FITZGERALD,
LIZI ATTWOOD, CHRISSIE SAUNDERS, ABI GOODMAN,
DR. SHERYL SORBY AND DR. JACOB HABGOOD.

CHILDREN FROM:
KING ALFRED SCHOOL
DEVONSHIRE HOUSE PREPARATORY SCHOOL
ST JAMES CHURCH OF ENGLAND PRIMARY SCHOOL

I'd like to thank the most remarkable women in my life: Thank you to my mum for teaching me independence and a belief that I can do anything. Thank you to my sister for teaching me compassion and kindness. And finally my daughter for giving me the opportunity to love someone more than I ever thought possible.

. . . .

LITTLE MISS GEEK'S PRIMARY FOCUS IS TO INSPIRE WOMEN AND YOUNG GIRLS TO BE CREATORS OF TECHNOLOGY.

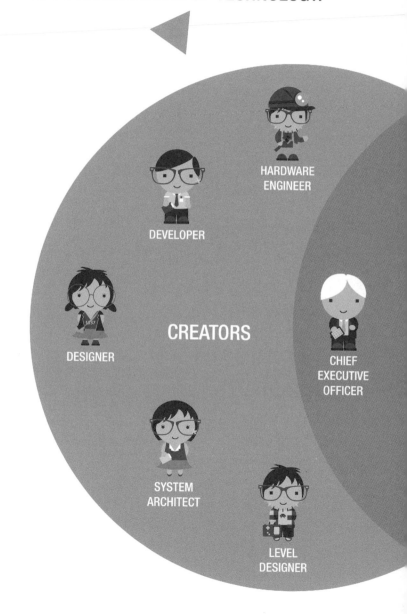

HARDWARE
ENGINEER

DEVELOPER

CREATORS

DESIGNER

CHIEF
EXECUTIVE
OFFICER

SYSTEM
ARCHITECT

LEVEL
DESIGNER

MARKETING
AND PR

PAYROLL

CHIEF
INFORMATION
OFFICER

SUPPORTERS

MANAGEMENT

ACCOUNTS

HUMAN
RESOURCES

THREE WORDS YOUNG GIRLS ASSOCIATE WITH INFORMATION TECHNOLOGY

YOU JOIN A COMPUTING CLASS!

ONLY 8% OF STUDENTS

WERE AWARDED TO WOMEN IN 2008

YOU GRADUATED!

ONLY 17% OF TECHNOLOGY JOBS

YOU GOT A JOB!

MORE WOMEN NEEDED IN TECH!

FINISH?

Less than 1 in 5 in the tech workforce are Women

Chapter

The Trouble With Tech

The doctor leaves the delivery room, finishing his notes on an iPad. A proud father texts his friends, emails his parents and tweets the first pictures of his new family. And in her mother's arms a newborn Little Miss Geek takes her first blinking look at the gadget-filled world she's been brought into. A little human filled with limitless potential. She has the power to do anything. Unfortunately statistics say that, right now, it probably won't have anything to do with technology.

Currently only seventeen percent of all technology jobs in the United Kingdom are held by women. *Seventeen percent*. Less than one in five.[5] In any industry that would be disappointing. In the industry that is shaping the future of mankind, that's downright criminal. Look around you – count the screens and gadgets in the room. Think about how many times you have used a computer today. We are living in the middle of a technological revolution and right now women are being left on the edge. This can't go on. It's unfair to women and it's damaging the industry.

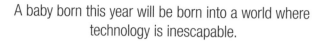

A baby born this year will be born into a world where technology is inescapable.

Currently only 17% of all tech jobs in the UK are held by women.[1]

UK homes have an average of over four devices connected to a home WiFi network.[6] Analogue television has been replaced by TiVo. More and more people now own a smartphone, a gadget with more processing power than the personal computers of a few years ago. Most gadgets have ceased to become gadgets – they're now just 'things'.

It astounds me how intuitive children are with new technology. When I first brought home my iPad – a gadget that still seems so futuristic to me that it takes my breath away – my kids picked it up like it was nothing, swooshing their fingers across the screen, finding out things about it that I never knew existed. A friend's two-year-old became so used to touchscreen technology that he couldn't understand why their flatscreen TV wouldn't respond to his slaps.

Of course it's always been the same – for adults who have seen the rise of a new technology, it takes a lot to stop it seeming like a magical accomplishment. For kids, who know no better, it simply represents normality. An iPad to a child born today is no different than a television, or a camera, or a light bulb.

Tech follows a lifespan that moves from exciting invention to expensive new product to everyday appliance. Cars, toasters, photocopiers, TV, the Internet. They all followed the same pattern. The thrilling difference with today's new trends is that this 'normalization' of powerful technology has recently encompassed computing. Where once a computer represented the ultimate in serious tech, it is now just another tool.

The idea of somebody being 'computer literate' – ever present on CVs until quite recently – has become obsolete. Children do not teach themselves how to use computers in the same way as they are taught to read. Rather, it is more like learning to walk or talk: an organic process that is an unavoidable part of their development. They are able to learn the necessary skills from interacting with the world around them – skills that are still taught to adults in night classes.

> By the time a child reaches school, they will have become 'computer literate' without even knowing it.

It all boils down to talking – children want to know how to communicate. Just as a child picks up his/her native language without even noticing, so too a child born today will learn how to compute without even knowing what a computer is. When my kids pick up the iPad, they are completely unaware of the decades of experimentation, design and innovation that have led to something so powerful becoming so accessible. For them it is just another part of their world. And if they think something as amazing as a tablet computer is run of the mill – just imagine what they might grow up to invent. The mind boggles. So what has this got to do with the matter in hand?

> What makes all this so exciting is that we are raising a generation of people that will take computing and technology to a level that we cannot even dream of.

All those tiny hands using screens and keyboards and motion sensors represent an incredible source of raw material for a tech industry that has the power to turn them from *consumers* into *creators*. All it takes is a little nudge in the right direction. As things stand, half of this potential is being thrown away.

It might come as a shock, but all these children born with a screen in their hands are actually made up of two sexes, not one. Boys and girls. Girls. Millions upon millions of girls who are natural techies – Little Miss Geek after Little Miss Geek using countless products designed by an industry that they'll never be a part of.

If past trends continue – and until something is done there's no indication that they won't – a huge chunk of these bright young technology users will be lost to other industries as young women choose not to translate their interest in gadgets into a career. Things need to change. For too long the world has sat back and thought of computers as 'boys' toys'.

For too long the industry has made no progress in killing off the image of I.T. workers as sweaty, antisocial, awkward men.

I'm sure if you asked any tech CEO they would tell you that they'd love to have a more diverse workforce, and I've never met an I.T. guy who boasts about the fact that he works with hardly any women.

The problem is not that women aren't wanted, but that they aren't made to feel wanted.

MYTH

MORE WOMEN BUYING TECH PRODUCTS WILL MEAN MORE WOMEN IN THE INDUSTRY.

FACT

DESPITE THE BOOM IN CONSUMERS, THE PERCENTAGE OF WOMEN IN TECH CAREERS IS DECREASING.

It is an issue that starts at childhood and continues throughout a woman's life – they are being given too many excuses to turn their back on the tech industry at every stage in their life. An effort needs to be made from grassroots up that tells Little Miss Geeks everywhere that technology is *the* industry to be in if you want to change the future. We have to target girls while they are young. We have to help them nurture their love of technology before society tells them that technology isn't for them.

• •

Why The Problem Isn't Going To Go Away On Its Own

Of course it would be very easy for us to sit back and do nothing, cross our fingers and hope the problem will go away and that women will start being interested in tech careers all on their own. Indeed, you'd be forgiven for thinking that this was a relatively logical position to take.

We're living in an age that is more dependent on technology than ever – and, as I've already mentioned, this means that both boys and girls are growing up with computers. There was a time when the stereotype of the computer as a 'boys' toy' was largely accurate. During the development of the PC industry in the Seventies and Eighties computers were not only built by men but – by and large – bought by men.

A Catch 22 ensued: Men bought tech products, so men made tech products, which meant more men bought tech products, which meant more men made tech products.

It was assumed that until more women were buying tech, the tech industry would continue its male-bias – through no fault of its own – and there was nothing that anyone could do about it. Now that heralded day has arrived: *Praise be! Women are finally buying technology!*

Four out of ten tech products are now bought by women.[2] One would have every reason to think that the cycle is about to be broken. Men wanted to build computers because men were the ones who bought computers. Now more women are buying computers, the same should apply to them, right?

The last decade saw a huge increase in the number of women aged 18-24 involved in home electronic purchases, a rise of 32% between 1998 and 2008.[2]

All the industry has to do is sit back and wait for these new tech consumers to become new tech creators. Sadly a very odd thing is happening. More and more women are buying technology products, and more and more young girls are growing up using computers, tablets, smartphones and the like. These figures keep increasing – which in itself is amazing.

But somehow, inexplicably, the percentage of women going into technology careers is currently falling. More users, less careers. It doesn't make any sense. Some of the stats are eye-watering:

Between 2001 and 2011 the percentage of tech jobs held by women *declined* from 22% to 17% in the UK.[1]

Between 2004 and 2011 the percentage of Computing A-Levels taken by women declined from 12% to 8% – the gap between men and women has widened eight percentage points.[8]

Between 1991 and 2008 the percentage of technology jobs held by women *declined* from 36% to 24% in the US.[9]

Between 1985 and 2008 the percentage of technology and science degrees awarded to women in the US *declined* by just under half, from 37% to 18%.[10]

There is one girl for every eleven boys in the average UK A-Level Computing class in 2011 – last year only 300 females took Computing.[11]

37%
1985

Technology and
Science Degrees
Awarded to Women

DECLINED!

18%
2008

Technology
Jobs Held By
Women in UK

22%
2001

DECLINED!

17%
2011

36%
1991

Technology
Jobs Held By
Women in US

DECLINED!

24%
2008

Computing
A-Levels Taken
By Women

12%
2004

DECLINED!

8%
2011

There was 1 girl for every 11 boys in the average UK A-Level Computing class in 2011.[11]

Given the raw potential that female tech users represent, anything other than a huge increase of women in tech jobs over the last decade would have represented a disappointment. So a decrease? *That's a catastrophe.*

What a confusing world our Little Miss Geek has been born into. On the one hand she's part of a tech savvy generation of women that have never been more plugged in – she will grow up with tech influencing her life in a way a girl born twenty years before could never have imagined. On the other hand, she's never been less likely to go into the industry herself.

What does this tell us? How can the technology industry not only be failing to convert women to its cause, but actually be driving them away?

Like many things, it's all about image. The disparity between female tech consumers and women going into the industry itself points to one, unavoidable conclusion:

The technology industry has an image problem.

Women love the Internet. They love their laptops, their tablets, their phones and their iPods. They use computers in every aspect of their lives. But for some reason the connection is not being made between the incredible products they use everyday and the companies that build them. Instead girls see the career as unappealing and dull – and in the job market, perception is everything. The nuts and bolts of what actually goes on in a tech company have little to do with what makes somebody want to work there – it's all about what they imagine goes on. For many women that's a boring, uncreative place that is dominated by men. Why on earth would they want to get involved?

Tech's dreadful image problem.

If we sit back and do nothing then the situation is not going to change. If anything, it's going to get worse. The industry needs to take a long hard look in the mirror and work out how to make itself more appealing to women. *Fast.*

The worst thing we can do is shrug our shoulders and assume that everything is alright as it is. To do this would be to ignore the vast potential that exists in an army of newly-minted Lady Geeks. The technological consumer base has evolved, *now the industry must, too.*

• •

REASONS WHY A CEO OF A TECHNOLOGY COMPANY SHOULD CARE

① DIVERSITY IS GOOD FOR BUSINESS.

② WOMEN ARE UNTAPPED CONSUMERS IN THE MARKET.

③ WOMEN ARE BUYING TECH PRODUCTS, BUT THEY'RE NOT YET USING THEM TO THEIR FULL POTENTIAL.

④ WOMEN REPRESENT A POOL OF RAW TECHNOLOGICAL TALENT.

⑤ IF YOU DON'T WAKE UP TO THIS NOW, YOUR COMPETITORS WILL.

Five Reasons Why A Technology CEO Should Care

Of course, it's all very well me banging on about this situation being unfair to women, but I'm a realist. I know that though everyone might agree, it doesn't give anyone any real incentive to change things.

We are talking about business after all – a social conscience is a luxury, especially when profits are involved. As we've discussed, more women are using technology than ever before. So long as the customer base is diverse, it doesn't matter what the makeup of the industry is, right?

4 out of 10 tech products are already bought by women.[2]

Technology has become so fundamental to all our lives that everybody, no matter what their gender, is going to buy it regardless of how it's designed and marketed. It's not like they've got any choice. Since four out of ten tech products are already bought by women, why on earth should the industry break a sweat to change things? Because it's the right thing to do? Give me a break. Most consumers don't give a hoot who builds their products, so long as they get the job done.

If I were a tech CEO I'd think the same thing. It's all very well appealing to fairness and justice and complaining about women being left out in the cold, but we shouldn't expect a company to do women any special favours without giving them solid evidence as to why a more diverse workforce would benefit them in the market. Thankfully there are plenty of *financial reasons* why the industry should aim to get more women in technology.

1. Diversity Is Good For Business.

Six friends are sitting in a restaurant. The waiter arrives, but instead of taking each of their orders individually he takes one diner aside – let's call him John – and discreetly asks him to choose what the whole table is having for dinner. After puzzling over the menu, John looks around the table and tries to imagine what dish best suits everybody.

As much as he would like to put himself inside each of their heads, to experience each of their taste buds, John is on his own. Denied the chance to ask each of them their opinion, he is forced to make an educated guess, based on his own experiences.

After a moment's reflection, he chooses the chicken. John's rationale for the decision goes something along the lines of: 'I've had the chicken before. I liked the chicken. I can't imagine a situation where somebody wouldn't like the chicken!'

Fair enough. When the food arrives, four of the table are happy and begin tucking into their food. The other two don't touch their meals. One, it turns out, simply doesn't like chicken. The other looks at John. 'Didn't you know? *I'm vegetarian!*'

It's not that John's choice was a particularly bad one – given the circumstances, keeping two thirds of the table happy is a decent result. But if he'd had the chance to canvas the group before his decision, to find out their likes and dislikes and get their input on the final decision, he could have made a choice that kept all six diners happy. Any product worth its salt is going to appeal to more than one particular type of person – and that's where it helps to have as many voices round the table as possible. The figures appear to back this up – a Catalyst report found that technology companies with more women on their management teams have a 34% higher return on investment.[12]

Tech companies with more women on their management teams have a 34% higher return on investment.[12]

It's not that women are any more effective or more talented than men – but they do provide different experiences and ask different questions. This can be invaluable when designing or marketing a new product – a male-heavy community risks losing out on valuable insight.

One of life's cruellest limitations is that for as long as we live we will never see the world from any perspective other than our own. We will never know how something tastes or feels to someone else. There is no person, no matter how skilled or qualified, that cannot benefit from another perspective. The more varied these perspectives – the more diverse the voices around the table - the better the product will be.

2. Women Are Untapped Consumers In The Market.

Any ambitious company should want to sell to as many people as possible. So women are already buying far more tech than they used to? Great. But is that enough for you? Can you just sit back and be content? The answer should most definitely be no. The Harvard Business Review has calculated that marketing to women represents a bigger financial opportunity

ACCORDING TO THE
HARVARD BUSINESS REVIEW,
MARKETING TO WOMEN
REPRESENTS A BIGGER
OPPORTUNITY THAN INDIA
AND CHINA COMBINED.[13]

than India and China combined.[13] There are huge piles of money out there waiting to be made, and whoever makes headway into the female market will reap the rewards.

If women are already prepared to buy products made almost exclusively by men, just imagine how many more technology products they would buy if they were being designed and marketed with them in mind.

As soon as the world stops selling tech products to women as 'boys' toys' that haven't been made for them (but that they've very kindly been allowed to buy and play with, thank-you very much) and starts making products that suit both genders, then the already fast-growing female market will come into its own.

To do this properly, there can be no room for guesswork. To get it right women need to be on the team. They need to be in the room, helping make the decisions that count. Achieve this and see those profits rise.

3. Women Are Buying Tech Products, But They're Not Yet Using Them To Their Full Potential.

So women are buying your product. You've got it into their hands. Congratulations. What now? For years technology has been as much about *the ecosystem* as it is about hardware. Take the iPod, the product that saved Apple and launched it on the road to world domination, emerging from a vast sea of competing MP3 players to boss the market into submission.

Yes, it was a sexy piece of kit. But what made the iPod such a success was iTunes – the software that made it easier than ever to purchase, download and transfer music.

The Amazon Kindle represents another good example. There are plenty of other, fancier e-Readers on the market, but millions upon millions of Kindles are sold because it taps into the Amazon ecosystem – which makes buying a book the most painless thing in the world.

Technology today is only partially about how something works to the touch of your fingers – it has to be intuitive in the way it interacts with the web as well. There's no point having a Ferrari if you can't drive it on the road. Imagine how much more interactive women would be with technology if the ecosystems were designed with more female input? If women feel *shut out* they are less likely to use products to their full potential, and thus less likely to spend money in the long term.

The more women we can have designing, building and maintaining these ecosystems, the easier the problems that are keeping women from using them will be identified, leading to a major increase in revenue over time.

4. Women Represent A Pool Of Raw Technological Talent.

One thing I want to make clear with this book is that the best way forward is not positive discrimination. As far as I'm concerned, any company that doesn't pick the best person for the job in hand – man or woman – is doing itself a disservice.

But currently the industry is not getting a fair choice. How can you know that you've got the best person for the job if you're being limited by who you can choose from? If you truly want to find the best candidate for a job, in any industry, you've got to keep your options open. Right now, with so many talented, enthusiastic young women turning their backs on technology in favour of other careers, anybody advertising for a technology job will find their pool severely limited.

A well-paid, interesting tech job for a successful company will attract hundreds of applicants, most of whom will be exceptionally talented at what they do. But currently most tech employers are forced to choose the best *man* for the job – not the best *person*.

The technology industry is continuing to grow, and without more female applicants it will find itself with more jobs than ever and not enough people qualified to fill them. What makes that prospect even worse is that most of the women turning their back on tech careers are technologically savvy. Not only are bright young minds slipping through the net, but these are bright young minds that are *interested in tech products.*

The perfect female employee is out there, and you've no chance of employing her because right now you can't even get her in the room. Make the technology industry a career that appeals to women, and suddenly you've doubled the talented individuals knocking on the door. More women means more applicants, means more talent. It's as simple as that.

5. If You Don't Wake Up To This Now, Your Competitors Will.

Sooner or later (one has to hope) the industry is going to wake up to the goldmine that lurks in the untapped potential of women and technology – both from a consumer and a talent perspective – and there will be a firefight to see who can make themselves most attractive to new graduates and new customers.

Any company that hasn't put in the legwork to make itself female-friendly will see their competitors holding a huge advantage – and may well be left behind. But if a company acts now and puts in a real concerted effort into making a technology career with them appealing to the best graduates – and not just the best male graduates – it will reap the benefits.

Acting on all of the points listed above would provide a company with an invaluable edge in a vastly competitive industry. Whoever can crack the nut first and find a way to make themselves a place that is genuinely exciting for talented Lady Geeks will see their rivals left behind, standing in the dust wondering where they went so wrong.

5

REASONS WHY A YOUNG WOMAN SHOULD CONSIDER A CAREER IN TECH

1. IT'S ONE OF THE MOST CREATIVE JOBS OUT THERE.

2. YOU WILL BE HELPING OTHER PEOPLE.

3. YOU DON'T HAVE TO HAVE A MAGNETIC ATTRACTION TO COMPUTERS.

4. IT'S ONE OF THE BEST-PAYING CAREERS FOR A WOMAN.

5. THIS IS YOUR FUTURE TOO.

Five Reasons Why A Young Woman Should Consider A Career In Technology

The key to the problem, however, lies not only in convincing the tech industry that it needs women — we must also convince women that they need the industry.

The tech industry's image problem means that girls are far more likely to be attracted to careers in PR, advertising, the arts and education. No matter how welcoming a tech company makes itself towards women, it will do no good at all unless this attitude can be reversed.

There are numerous reasons why girls seem less attracted to careers in technology than boys — and we will go into them in more detail later in the book. We'll also delve further into some of the qualities that make it an incredibly attractive industry to work in — and burst a few myths about technology's image along the way.

For now though, let's briefly highlight a few of the reasons why any intelligent, ambitious young woman should consider a tech career. Start effectively getting these across to girls everywhere, and we'll be well on the way to ending the gender imbalance.

1. It's One Of The Most Creative Jobs Out There.

The same rationale that at school leads more girls to choose arts and humanities subjects over science and maths, makes them excited by industries that offer a chance to exercise

80% of women want creative, independent job roles. Only 30% of women believe that tech jobs can provide such an opportunity.[14]

creative talents. While a man is more likely to be attracted to qualities like stability, reputation, salary and career progression, a woman is more likely to chase down a job she feels will interest and stimulate her intellectually.

Any industry that (at least in appearance) offers the chance to express oneself and to work with words or images has a huge advantage when it comes to attracting female graduates. This often results in young women gravitating towards industries like the arts, publishing, advertising and PR – but not technology.

For many women tech is often lumped in with job-descriptions like 'accounting', 'finance' or 'statistics' as a by-word for dreary, Orwellian office-based dronedom. The I.T. geek, sat alone at his computer, watching the ones and zeros whizzing by day after day until his eyes start to water and his brain starts to melt.

A study by Cisco in 2009 found that eighty percent of girls want the chance to be creative and independent in their work environment – but only thirty percent believed a job in I.T. could provide them with such an opportunity.[14] Technology's dreadful image problem strikes again.

How can the industry that is shaping the future of the modern world ever be considered uncreative?

Technology is far from a perfect science. It's not simply about pressing button A and then pressing button B. It is about

MYTH

YOU HAVE TO BE OBSESSED WITH COMPUTERS TO WORK IN TECHNOLOGY.

FACT

THE INDUSTRY IS FOR EVERYONE, NOT JUST THE MOST OBSESSIVE.

90% of women want jobs that help people. 60% of women believe that tech jobs do not fit this role.[15]

language, design, building, marketing, playing and inventing. It's about teamwork and problem solving. It's about noticing something that the world is lacking and then giving it to them. The tech industry doesn't stifle ingenuity, it thrives on it – and any girl with a creative streak would struggle to find a better, more exciting home.

2. You Will Be Helping Other People.

Alongside creativity, the other priority for women when it comes to career choice is the chance to help others. Industries like medicine, education, charity or the public sector often prove attractive to women because they offer the chance to provide a service to society – to improve the lives of others.

Cisco found that ninety percent of girls are looking for a job that can do this – but again, only sixty percent of them believe I.T. would provide them with the opportunity.[15]

What's worse – and arguably more harmful – is that less than half of *parents* and *teachers* see a tech career as a job that enables somebody to help others. If young girls' role models don't believe it, then why should the girls themselves?

But if these girls, or their teachers and parents, stopped for a moment to think about what technology actually does, they would realise how short-sighted an attitude that is. Okay, so it might not have the same hands-on, caring-for-others feel to it that comes with medicine or teaching, but the technology industry represents a way to help people on a global scale.

It's about communication. It's about information. It's about helping people learn, about helping them work, about helping them talk and about helping them have fun.

The builders of tomorrow's tech have the power to change people's lives for the better in numerous ways. Their work can help others not on a one-to-one level, but at a scale of millions at a time.

Only thirty percent of girls believed a job in I.T. could provide them a creative and independent job opportunity.[14]

3. You Don't Have To Have A 'Magnetic Attraction' To Computers.

We all know somebody like it. The guy who rebuilt his mum's computer at age four. The one who still keeps an old Atari 2600 – in mint condition - in his bedroom. The guy who'd rather die than use Windows over Linux.

Computers and tech have always been associated with a certain type of extreme interest, attracting a passion and devotion that is unique, and leading to the rise in geek subculture that came to define the computing age.

Of course that's all absolutely fine, and the industry would be nowhere were it not for super tech-savvy gadget-men. Where the problem comes in is that it can often be hard for other, slightly less passionate people to express an interest in technology. It's become the norm to assume that unless you are that sort of computer-obsessed, coding-straight-out-of-the-womb type of nerd then the technology industry isn't a place you belong. Unfortunately it's girls whom this attitude is hurting the most. It's been demonstrated that boys and girls develop a love of computers in very different ways. Young boys who become interested in technology are much more likely to develop this type of passion from an early age. In their book 'Unlocking the Clubhouse' Jane Margolis and Allan Fisher describe what they term 'the magnetic attraction'.[16]

> *There is a subset of boys and men who burn with a passion for computers and computing. Through the intensity of their interest, they both mark the field as male and enshrine in its culture their preference for single-minded intensity and focus on technology.*

75% of men fit the magnetic attraction profile. Only 25% of women have the same qualities.[16]

Margolis and Fisher found that three quarters of men fit this magnetic attraction profile, but only a quarter of women have the same qualities. This can be off-putting for girls, who tend to develop a love of technology more gradually, over time. When they first use a computer they don't necessarily want to start tinkering, reprogramming, looking at its innards – which is, of course, completely normal.

But when faced with a group of boys that want to do all of these things, it can be pretty intimidating. This often means they disregard their own (on the surface) less passionate interest as not good enough for a career in the industry. They shut up, keep quiet and let the boys do all the talking, content in the knowledge that if they really wanted to work in technology, they would be far more passionate about computing. Rubbish. This 'magnetic attraction' is not a pre-requisite of a career in technology – *you do not need to live and breathe computers.*

IT IS **NOT** ABOUT DEMANDING THAT COMPANIES HIRE MORE WOMEN, IT'S ABOUT CHANGING THINGS SO THAT MORE **WOMEN WANT TO BE HIRED.**

What you need is, like any field, a keen mind, a willingness to learn and a healthy interest – the industry is for everyone, not just for the most vocal.

There are a great number of women who don't believe they have any real interest in technology – and yet these same people will coo over the latest smartphone in the pub, marvel over their friend's new smart television, or surf the web for hours on end. It's an industry that makes as many of our toys as it does our tools, and this means that anyone entering it today will have a far greater base level of knowledge than somebody twenty years ago. That's more than enough for anyone to get started – so don't let the super-geeks put you off.

4. It's One Of The Best-Paying Careers For A Woman.

Though there is a great disparity in terms of the number of men and women in tech, the same thing cannot be said of the pay gap. Because it is a (relatively) new industry, technology appears to have less of a financial glass ceiling for women than many other industries. A study by Forbes found that of the ten best-paying jobs for a woman in 2011, three of them were based in the tech industry.[17] It's a growing industry that is hungry for talented people – and will reward them handsomely, male or female.

5. This Is Your Future Too.

Last but not least, the most important reason. Computing and technology is already a massive part of our lives. As we go forward that influence is only going to continue.

The next generation of technology innovators are going to be the people who shape the future. They will dictate how we interact with each other and with the world around us. We will use their inventions in every aspect of our lives.

At the moment this future will be written (mostly) by men.

This can't be allowed to happen. We can't have one gender sitting back and watching the world evolve while the other makes all the frontline decisions. Unless more women can be convinced to start showing a serious interest in the tech industry they will forfeit their vote in deciding what comes next.

Tim Berners-Lee. Bill Gates. Steve Jobs. Larry Page. Mark Zuckerberg. Sergei Brin. For too long women have been absent among the game-changers. No longer. More women going into technology will mean more women shaping the future, which will be a wonderful thing. Not because a woman's opinion is any better than a man's, but because at the end of the day, it's their world too and they should have a say in what happens to it.

So there we have it. This, of course, is easier said than done. To do this effectively there are no short-term measures. You can't just employ more women for the sake of it. We have to change attitudes about technology.

· ·

What Needs To Happen

Currently only 17% of technology jobs in the UK are held by women.[1] Women make up half of all potential technology users, they should make up half of the industry as well.

We have to burst myths about the industry. It's not a *'boys' game'*. It's not boring. It can change the world. You don't have to be obsessed with computers to go into it. With this book I want to help the technology industry build a lasting connection with young women growing up 'geek'.

From childhood, through school and university and even at the core of tech companies themselves, we need to make it clear that this no longer needs to be a male industry.

We want women and need women to be among the pioneers that are building the future.

There's a long road ahead, but if we can start changing the image of the technology industry and getting these ideas across, I have every faith that women will indeed become the pioneers of the future.

THE **INDUSTRY** NEEDS TO TAKE A LONG HARD **LOOK** IN THE MIRROR AND WORK OUT **HOW TO MAKE ITSELF** MORE **APPEALING TO WOMEN.**

FAST.

BOYS PLAY WITH LEGO

GIRLS PLAY WITH DOLLS

BOYS WORK IN GAMING

GIRLS WORK IN PR

BOYS CREATE TECH

GIRLS USE TECH

BOYS FIX TECH

GIRLS NEED TECH FIXED

Chapter

Maybe She's Born With It...

Wrapping paper is strewn across the floor, a half-eaten birthday cake sits in the fridge, and exhausted parents are slumped on the sofa. And playing with her toys at the centre of it all is our Little Miss Geek, who has just turned two. At this age the world is at its most magical than it will ever be again. Every toy, every event and every interaction presents a new opportunity for her to discover what sort of person she's going to be.

But how much is she actually in control of her future? Is there anything that would make her more likely to go into the technology industry? Or have her chromosomes already made the decision for her? First let's get the obvious out of the way. Men and women are different. There's no getting round it. While I have no intention of telling the Little Miss Geeks out there to sit back and accept their fate, it would be remiss of me to go further without acknowledging some of the psychological differences that exist between the male and female brains. It does more harm than good to put on rose-tinted glasses and pretend that men and women are the same in every way. They're not, and there's no shame in admitting that. But what makes men act like men and women act like women?

How much of it is cultural, and how much dependant on the way we are wired at birth?

One of the most controversial topics in psychology is the extent to which experiential factors and biological factors determine the way our sexes behave. For a long time it was considered taboo to discuss inherent biological differences between boys and girls. The fear was it would encourage sexist discrimination and may lead to the idea that 'men are superior to women' gaining some semblance of scientific credibility. In recent times, however, the debate seems to have cooled. There is more of an acceptance that men and women are both better at certain things. This doesn't mean that one gender is better than the other overall, but instead (speaking generally) both possess *small advantages in different areas.*

Simon Baron-Cohen is Professor of Developmental Psychopathology in the departments of Psychiatry and Experimental Psychology at the University of Cambridge. He is well known for his research on the characteristics of the male and female brain. Baron-Cohen's 'E-S theory' – outlined in his book 'The Essential Difference'[18] – makes the distinction between two types of psychological behaviour: *empathizing* and *systemizing.* He posits that most people are born with one of three common brain types:

TYPE E

People born with type 'E brains' are hard-wired to be stronger at empathizing than systemizing. They are better equipped to identify another person's emotions and respond to these appropriately. According to Baron-Cohen, the 'empathizer' 'intuitively figures out how people are feeling, and how to treat people with care and sensitivity'. He refers to this as the 'female brain', because more females than males show these characteristics on average.

TYPE S

Type 'S brains' are hard-wired to be stronger 'systemizers' than empathizers. They are better equipped to understand and build systems, and carry out tasks that require mental rotation. Baron-Cohen says that the systemizer 'intuitively figures out how things work, or what the underlying rules are controlling a system'. This is referred to as the 'male brain', because it appears more commonly in men.

TYPE B

Other individuals are equally strong in their systemizing and empathizing qualities. Baron-Cohen refers to this as the 'balanced brain'.

Baby girls spent more time looking at a face and baby boys more time looking at a mechanical mobile.[19]

He has found that baby girls as young as twelve months old respond more empathetically than boys of the same age to the distress and upset of others – showing more sad looks, comforting actions and sympathetic sounds.

How much influence 'nurture' has on these differences is very difficult to quantify – are these girls showing more empathy because of the way that their brains are wired, or because of environmental factors that have already begun to have an impact? Baron-Cohen cites a Cambridge University study which showed that at one day old – before any experiential conditioning had taken place – baby girls spent more time looking at a face and baby boys more time looking at a mechanical mobile.[19] The same team found that hormones play a part – toddlers who had lower foetal testosterone levels presented higher levels of eye contact.

While he admits that culture and socialisation play a large part in whether a person develops a 'male brain' or a 'female brain', he says that studies like this show that biology is also partly involved.

Now before you bite my head off, I don't believe that this empathizer/systemizer category applies to everybody. I know plenty of men who are excellent empathizers and a great number of women who work with complex systems every day. I would never encourage anybody to take a study like Baron-Cohen's as gospel – Gender Psychology is a hotly contested field and there are alternative studies that have challenged his claims.[20] But since he admits that the theory is not about stereotyping gender, but about helping us understand why individuals are considered typical or atypical for their sex, I am happy to concede that it may give us some clue as to why a career like technology (which, on the surface, would appear to rely greatly on being a good systemizer) may be seen as a predominantly male profession.

If, as a general rule, men are more likely to possess the 'S' characteristic then it follows that they will be more likely to follow a career path that utilises systemization. Similarly if women are more likely to possess the 'E' characteristic they will be more likely to follow a career path that involves empathy and human interaction – such as PR, teaching or medicine. But should we sit back and accept this?

Does our biology control our destiny?

One could look at a study like Baron-Cohen's and make the assumption that many women have been born without the tool kit to work with technology. But right now tech – which is as much about reaching people, communication and teamwork as it is about logic, programming and systems – should be a place where the 'female brain' can feel at home.

Part of the problem is that since technology is predominantly staffed by men, the criteria that tech companies look for in employees are still based on traditional 'male characteristics'. *Male brains seeking male brains seeking male brains.*

Raising awareness can help change this.

Many girls growing up around technology may be unaware that their gender (or sex, depending on your point of view) might make them interact differently with tech than their male counterparts. The 'E-S theory' may also go some way to explaining Margolis and Fisher's 'magnetic attraction' that I mentioned in the previous chapter. If the 'S-type' 'male brain' is wired to have an affinity with mechanical systems, it's only natural that boys should show an early passion for computers. It's also natural that girls – who are more likely to have an 'E-type' brain, and therefore less likely to show this passion – look for careers that involve social interaction and helping others.

What if, however, girls and boys were made more aware of these differences? Would it change the way they behave? If our Little Miss Geek knew that her lack of a burning passion for technology was the result of the 'female brain' she has been born with, and not a lack of a natural aptitude, she might be less likely to abandon tech at the earliest possible opportunity. Biology obviously plays a part in determining who you become – but that's not to say its definitive.

Ultimately, where our Little Miss Geek ends up is up to her.

We shouldn't be afraid to admit that men and women are born with certain differences. The problem comes when these differences are manipulated to create stereotypes that damage the chances of women taking certain career paths.

MYTH

BOYS ARE BORN WITH MORE NATURAL MATHEMATICAL AND SCIENTIFIC ABILITY THAN GIRLS.

FACT

THE ONLY THING THAT HOLDS GIRLS BACK IS THIS OUTDATED STEREOTYPE.

Maths Class Is Tough!

In 1992, toy company Mattel caused an uproar when it released 'Teen Talk Barbie', a talking version of the doll whose catchphrases included – brace yourselves – 'I love shopping!' and 'Will we ever have enough clothes?'[21] Shudder. But the phrase that caused most consternation – and forced Mattel into a very hasty U-turn in which all the offending models were recalled – was 'Math class is tough!'

Excuse me while I struggle to keep my breakfast down. Yet we shouldn't be too harsh on poor old Barbie – all she was doing was playing up to the long held stereotype that girls and mathematics just don't get along. Mathematics being a male ability is often cited as a reason why the technology industry is a masculine area.

But how true is it? Are boys actually born better equipped for STEM subjects (Science, Technology, Engineering and Mathematics), or is this merely the product of being raised in a culture that proclaims them more mathematically and scientifically capable before they've even picked up a pencil. This stereotype has become increasingly inaccurate over the past three decades, as girls have caught up with boys at the top of the mathematics tree – the ratio of boys to girls among children identified as *'mathematically precocious'* has plummeted in recent years, far quicker than it would have taken a genetic change to travel through the population.[22]

But if this is the case, why then do so few girls believe that they are suited for the subjects – particularly when placed in direct competition with boys? The negative stereotype is self-perpetuating. If girls grow up in a world that tells them they are worse than boys at maths and technology, *then those girls will believe that they are worse at maths and technology.*

In 1995 a study identified the phenomenon of 'stereotype threat' – the threat of being viewed by others in light of a negative stereotype and doing something, however small, that would lead to this stereotype being re-inforced.[23] If a girl takes a maths test in a room full of boys, she will worry and stress much more about the task in front of her than if she was surrounded by other girls.

Why should girls apply themselves to a subject in which the world believes that they are biologically predisposed to come second best? It's a horrible catch 22. If technology is going to convince our young women to join the industry they are going to have to stamp out negative stereotypes. By emphasising that girls and boys can, under the right conditions, achieve equally well in subjects like Maths and Science, it's going to have to stamp out any negative associations girls might have with the subjects. If they can begin to learn how good they are, they'll start to apply themselves more.

Male and female differences are something to be celebrated – and should never be a burden to either gender. Even proven differences that might be considered disadvantages have been shown to be easily remedied. What our girls need to realise is that the brain can be trained.

'GIRLS SEE COMPUTING AS UNFEMININE.'

DAME WENDY HALL,
PROFESSOR OF COMPUTER SCIENCE AT
THE UNIVERSITY OF SOUTHAMPTON.

Spatial Awareness:
Let's Level The Playing Field

One of the few significant gender gaps in terms of natural intelligence is found in the area of spatial awareness – particularly with regards to mental rotation.[24] *In his study, Baron-Cohen attributes this to strong spatial ability being linked to the 'systemizing' brain – that is most commonly found in boys.*

Spatial skills – the ability to picture and interact with the world around us – are seen as key to careers in science and tech. A 1994 study showed that a persons spatial visualisation ability is directly linked to his/her competence at interacting with computer software and interfaces.[25] When building and designing phones, websites and computers an ability to accurately picture all parts of the product in your head can come in very handy. You know the sort of test – *'if weird shape A is rotated one hundred and eighty degrees to the left, does it become weird shape B, C or D?'* For some deep-rooted evolutionary reason, women tend to have slightly more trouble answering. It's the same mental characteristic that has led to umpteen stand-up comics doing routines about women's map-reading ability.

Fine. As I said, men and women are different. The problem arises because this difference is never openly addressed. Girls who have often been near or at the top of a class up to a point in their education may suddenly find themselves struggling with high-level lab work and design. What's worse is that more often than not they fail to understand why.

MYTH

GIRLS LACK THE SPATIAL AWARENESS SKILLS FOR A CAREER IN TECHNOLOGY AND THERE'S NOTHING WE CAN DO ABOUT IT.

FACT

TRAINING AND THE RIGHT TOYS MEAN IT DOESN'T HAVE TO BE A DISADVANTAGE.

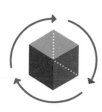

**Spatial
Awareness.**

Assuming that they're not cut out for the work, they begin to give up and leave it to the boys. This provides an easy excuse for the tech industry – *women don't start tech careers because they don't have the spatial skills to compete.*

But an excuse is exactly what it is.

Although I'm not disputing the fact that on average men are born with a greater capacity for spatial awareness and mental rotation, this is a problem that is easily remedied. Studies have shown that spatial awareness can be developed, to a competent level, through simple training exercises, and that this in turn can lead to the retention of women on technology courses. Dr. Sheryl Sorby, an Engineering professor at Michigan Technological University, first became interested in the problem when she had trouble as a student with a graphics class involving spatial tasks.[26,27,28]

Despite having a great aptitude for engineering, she found she was struggling and couldn't work out why. Teaching the same class a few years later, she realised that many of her female students were coming to her and describing the same difficulties. The young women believed they simply weren't cut out for the technological field, and wanted to leave the course. Test results gave the answer. When Sorby's first year engineering students were administered a spatial visualisation exam, the women were shown to be well behind the men. Of the students who failed the exam outright, *forty-three percent* were women – even though they made up only seventeen percent of the group taking the test. Furthermore, of the forty-five students who managed to record a perfect score, only *three* were women. Determined to do something about it, Sorby put together a ten-week course in spatial-visualisation for those with poorly developed spatial skills. Her results were remarkable, with students on her course improving their scores in spatial skills tests by over sixty percent. Even more encouraging were the long term results: more than three-quarters of female students who had taken the course remained in the School of Engineering, compared with just one half of those who had not. Sorby's work shows that spatial-visualisation is something that can be trained. As long as we pay attention to this minor deficiency, it would appear that there's absolutely no reason why it can't be overcome.

It's just a case of acknowledging the problem and levelling the playing field.

There can often be a nervousness around highlighting differences in the way genders learn and work – people are often afraid of seeming prejudiced or playing the victim.

Yet while this particular difference is left unspoken and untreated, our potential Lady Geeks will continue to think – wrongly – that maybe they just aren't smart enough for a career in tech. Let's change the attitude. Let's start explaining to young people that spatial skills aren't an unchangeable part of their make-up, but are an ability that can be developed over time. We need to make sure that our girls know that there is *absolutely nothing wrong with them.*

Toys Hold The Answer

The problem – and therefore part of the solution – lies in the world of play. Before they have even reached school, girls are at a double disadvantage. Not only have they been born with slightly underdeveloped spatial awareness, they are denied the chance to develop these skills due to the toys that they are traditionally given.

A gender
neutral toy.

Baron-Cohen cites children's toy choices as evidence of the difference between the 'male' and 'female' brains. His research found that when given the choice of toys, boys are instantly attracted to cars and construction kits (systemizing toys), while more girls than boys will go for dolls, enacting social and emotional themes.

So far, so obvious. Anyone who has raised a boy and a girl – as I have – would be able to tell you that much without picking up a scientific paper. There are 'boys' toys' and there are 'girls' toys'. That's just the way it goes. But it's a chicken and egg scenario. What happened first? Did boys play with Lego because they were better systemizers or did they become better systemizers because they always played with Lego?

Toys that involve taking things apart and putting them back together, those that allow the child to explore inner mechanics and those that encourage building new items, all help refine a child's spatial abilities from a young age. Extended play with a toy like Lego can make a huge difference to problem solving abilities, something that pays dividends years down the line in lab work and design. Similarly (a million mothers will want to kill me for saying this) three-dimensional video games have been shown to enhance mental rotation, as well as proving very useful when it comes to building skills in computing and design.[29]

But traditionally both construction toys and games controllers are often placed in the hands of boys – the gender already in possession of keen spatial awareness skills. This means that the boys get better and better while the girls get left behind – a problem that rears its ugly head once both sexes are in education and studying science and technology subjects.

Three-dimensional video games have been proven to enhance mental rotation, as well as proving very useful when it comes to building skills in computing and design.[29]

Baron-Cohen argues that more boys are innately attracted to these systemizer toys, but we can't ignore the experiential factors. The way our culture is set up plays a huge part in dictating gender behaviour, even at such a young age. We only have to look at the way they are marketed to see why construction toys are seen as being for boys.

Let's take Lego as an example. Those lovable, spiky Scandinavian bricks, the bane of barefooted parents the world over, have been delighting children since the 1940s, yet as a concept there is nothing that marks it out as being particularly 'male'. They are neutral, multicoloured and – despite accompanying instructions – possess the potential to be made into any number of objects.

The beautiful thing about Lego is it can be anything the child wants it to be. Yet despite this apparent neutrality, Lego sets are always placed in the 'boys' aisle' in the toy store. It's a troubling assumption to make. It's construction! It's building things! And racing things! And making a mess! It must be a 'boy's toy', *right?!*

For years Lego maintained that there was no gender bias in their products and marketed to both boys and girls. That was until 2005, when a downturn in profits forced them to rethink their strategy. Now they market the majority of their products directly to boys and boys alone, while girls are targeted with a pinker, cutesier set of kits.

It's a sad state of affairs, but one that has rewarded the company with an increase in revenue of 105% since 2006.[30] By playing up to the suspicions of Mars/Venus-obsessed parents, the company was able to save itself. But by conforming to stereotypes it risks causing a far bigger problem.

I don't want to be excessively harsh in my criticism of Lego – it's merely emblematic of a much wider problem, and we can hardly blame them for bending to the will of the market. We live in a world where parents believe that there are 'boys' toys' and there are 'girls' toys', and changing that is a huge task that isn't going to happen any time soon.

But it's putting girls at a disadvantage. 'Boys' toys' prepare a child better for a life dealing with careers such as technology, engineering, medicine and science while many 'girls' toys' prepare girls for lives as homemakers.

'I'D RATHER BE A DUSTBIN MAN THAN WORK IN I.T..'

MILLY, AGED 12,
ST. JAMES CHURCH OF ENGLAND
PRIMARY SCHOOL,
LONDON.

It's an attitude that is hampering our Little Miss Geeks at the first hurdle.

Boys have Lego, and girls have Barbie and princesses. Who's getting the better deal? One has been proven to build up mathematical ability and spatial awareness, as well as a penchant for construction, design, creativity and independent thought. *The other cultivates a love of all things pink and fluffy.*

If we can encourage girls from a young age to play with construction toys and (age appropriate) computer games, we can help them develop their spatial skills and make sure that they are not miles behind the boys once they get to school.

Perhaps, with time, we can get more boys and girls moving from the polarised 'E-S' 'male' and 'female' brains to the middle ground 'B' type.

Of course, none of this will happen unless we burst the myth of the most damaging 'boys' toy' of them all.

• •

Killing Off The 'Boys' Toy'

For decades a childhood fascination with computers was, almost exclusively, a boyish pastime. Computers were built by men for men. It is boys, rather than girls, who still see a computer as 'toys'.

A computer is in many ways like a Lego kit. Something that all kids can play with, regardless of gender. Something that any child with an active imagination could use in his or her own way. And yet when push comes to shove, it is *something that is aimed at and played with by boys.*

Girl or boy toy?

It's the same principle that sees science kits, microscopes or geology sets placed in the 'boys' aisle'. It's a by-product of some outdated and slightly scary prejudices. *'That's far too complicated for a tiny woman's brain! It's science! Give it to the men!'*

A computer is too complex. It's made up from a multitude of tiny parts. It let's you shoot people on Doom. *Definitely a 'boys' toy'!* Computers and their innards hold no fascination for little girls – why should they? And anyway, even if they did, it's not like they would understand!

It's an attitude that starts in childhood and stretches throughout adult life. How many men's magazines are littered with gadget guides and tech previews? And how few women's magazines do the same, unless it's listing 'Top Gifts For Your Man for Xmas'?

Somehow computers have never been classed as a 'toy' for girls.

A work tool, sure. Something to communicate with, okay. But never, ever a toy. What is a toy to a child? Something they play with. Something they love. An object that can act as a transmitter for their imaginations, that stimulates their minds and their dreams.

It's a quality that boy after boy has seen in computers for generations. From home transistor radio sets to the Xbox 360, little boys have always had fun with boxes of wires. Most girls, on the other hand, have traditionally taken very little interest, growing up to use them for work and functionality and the odd game on the train.

As recently as 2009, a NIC study asking boys to think of words they associated with computers came up with a list that included words like 'design', 'games' and 'video'. And the girls? 'Typing', 'math' and 'boredom'.[31]

When I spoke to a class of ten-year-old girls about the technology industry I found the same thing. Talk about gadgets – tablets, smartphones and the like – and the girls' eyes lit up, saying how fun and exciting they were. But mention computers and I.T. and suddenly the mood dropped. Choice quotes included 'people who work in I.T. don't want to go outside' and 'I'd rather be a dustbin man than work in I.T.'. If girls are growing up seeing computers as boring grown-up tools, while boys are growing up seeing them as toys –

AS RECENTLY AS 2009, WHEN AN NIC STUDY ASKED BOYS TO THINK OF WORDS THEY ASSOCIATED WITH COMPUTERS THEY CAME UP WITH 'DESIGN', 'GAMES' AND 'VIDEO'. AND THE GIRLS? 'TYPING', 'MATH' AND 'BOREDOM'.[31]

with all the potential for fun and excitement that this association brings – is it any wonder that boys are more likely to want to know how they are built?

Of course they want to go into the technology industry. It's a chance to play with toys all day long! Innovation is bred from imagination after all. So is this male gadget fetish – the 'magnetic attraction' so lacking in girls – something that resides in boys from birth? Or is it a product of a society that gives boys the Lego bricks and girls the Barbie Dreamhouse?

What would happen if girls were raised to treat computers in the same way as boys?

Kate Craig-Wood is a British I.T. entrepreneur and the co-founder of the UK's first carbon-neutral ISP, Memset. A strong advocate for the cause of women in technology, Craig-Wood ended up in the industry after being influenced by an older brother and a father who were both heavily interested in technology (her father was also a technology entrepreneur). She began programming at the age of nine, and by the time she reached thirteen was building her own software and hardware.

Craig-Wood is also uniquely placed to comment on the differences between the way boys and girls are encouraged to behave around computers. Until 2006, when she underwent a transsexual transition, Craig-Wood had been born and was living as a man. She says that this played a huge part in her burgeoning interest in technology as a child – due to her exterior appearance, her parents and teachers encouraged her to use computers: 'Because of my male body' she says 'I was encouraged to use tech a lot more than my sister. I grew up less fearful of testing and experimenting with computers – something I feel a lot of girls lack.'

Whether Craig-Wood would have followed the same career path had she been born in a female body is impossible to know – but her experiences highlight the impact that socialisation has on developing a technological interest. Craig-Wood was programming at age nine, something unheard of for most girls of that age, because it is simply not seen as a fun activity for a young girl to undertake, by parents or children alike. As soon as computers and other gadgets start to lose their 'boys' toy' tag with parents, it's my guess that we'll see a lot more young girls treating technology with more affection. So how do we start to overturn the long held stereotypes and prejudices about how our children play?

To win kids' hearts you must first win round their mums and dads.

We need to convince parents that computers are good for all children – not just for boys. Thankfully there has never been a better time to do so. It's inevitable that our parents have a huge influence on what we hold important in life, and their values directly affect our own choices throughout adulthood. Therefore if a parent doesn't believe – however subconsciously – that technology is worth their little girl caring about then it will take a miracle for that little girl to care about it in the future.

The problem is an old one. For decades computers and their close cousins – video games, mobiles, TVs – have been blacklisted as *'bad for children'*. Anything with a screen has long held negative connotations when it comes to raising our kids. How many times do we trot out the fears that our offspring will end up with 'square eyes', that too much screen-time will 'rot their brains'? (This in spite of the fact that most adults spend vast percentage of our time glued to one screen or another. 'Do as I say, not as I do' springs to mind).

When children grow up with their parents equating time using computers with being anti-social or lazy, is it any wonder that so many choose to disassociate themselves from computing as soon as possible? This is particularly true of young girls, for whom being sociable and communicative hold incredible importance.

The negativity is extraordinarily hard to shake off. As a parent I hate the feeling I get when my kids watch TV or are glued to the computer. When I see them slumped there, zombied out in front of the screen, it's very hard not to feel guilty. I should be doing more to get them out of the house. Pump them full of fresh air. I bet all parents feel the same. But times are changing. Screens are now the default way that our children will learn and play with the world – and parents need to start waking up to that. Games consoles are now providing interactive 'stand-up and play' learning experiences, while tablets and e-readers are giving publishers and authors an incredible platform to develop a new type of story book.

'BECAUSE OF MY MALE BODY I WAS ENCOURAGED TO USE TECH A LOT MORE THAN MY SISTER. I GREW UP LESS FEARFUL OF TESTING AND EXPERIMENTING WITH COMPUTERS – SOMETHING I FEEL A LOT OF GIRLS LACK.'

KATE CRAIG-WOOD,
CO-FOUNDER OF MEMSET.

As soon as parents begin to give these sort of technological learning experiences the same credibility as a favourite childhood book or toy, the sooner we will see more girls (and boys) treating technology as something magical and inspirational that they want to be a part of. Parents too will start seeing the benefits of a career in tech, and will start encouraging (consciously or unconsciously) their children to follow that path.

Most importantly, computers have now moved out of the bedroom and study, and into our hands. They are small enough to hold. They operate by touch. They are made to be played with. They are now unavoidable from an early age, regardless of old-school gender stereotypes. We need to start translating this accessibility into playtime. There is the potential – if we play our cards right over the next couple of decades – to have both little boys and little girls thinking of computers as things to be played with as well as worked on.

• •

Biology Isn't Everything

Perhaps the best evidence against the argument that women are born without the skills to thrive in the technology industry can be found by casting our eyes abroad. We've discussed at length how women are outnumbered in tech careers and tech degree courses in both the UK and the US.

If it really was natural for women to avoid careers in technology, if their genetic profile really did make them ill-suited to the industry, then surely this same imbalance would be reflected in technology companies over the world? But in some countries, where technology and computing are more favourably looked upon as careers for women, the gender imbalance is practically nonexistent.

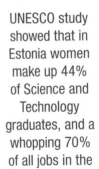

UNESCO study showed that in Estonia women make up 44% of Science and Technology graduates, and a whopping 70% of all jobs in the sector.[33]

The Baltic states –Estonia, Lithuania and Latvia – have not only achieved equality, there are actually more women than men in tech careers and in senior research posts at technology institutions.[32] In Estonia, the EU leader, a UNESCO study showed that women make up forty-four percent of science and technology graduates, and account for a whopping seventy percent of all jobs in the sector.[16] If women were born with a natural disadvantage, how could this ever happen? So what does this tell us?

It would appear that, despite the differences that exist between the 'male' and the 'female' brain, culture and environment play as much of a part in our destinies as biology. If going into technology were merely a matter of whether you're born a systemizer or an empathizer, then figures like those cited for Estonia would never be achieved anywhere. As far as I'm concerned this is great news, as it shows that there is something we can do. We can't change biology – but we can change cultural attitudes.

Our ideas about gender, old stereotypes about what men and women are good at and the toys we give our boys and our girls, are contributing factors that make our society, right now, a place that doesn't develop its young girls for tech careers. *It's time to wake up.* It's time to stop using stereotypes as an excuse. It's time to realise that women have as much right to play a part in technology as men. We've already taken the first step – girls now have a screen in front of them before they can talk. Now it is time to take that new-found tech fluency and nurture it. Our girls need to know that there is nothing wrong with them. There is room in the industry for both empathizers and systemizers. There is no major genetic defect that makes them unsuited to technology – they just deal with technology differently from boys.

Our Little Miss Geek is waiting to be mobilised. She can be a leader of her field. An innovator. A guru. But only if we start believing in her. Right from the beginning. Do that, and we'll begin to see results. Unfortunately, what comes next has the potential to undo all our hard work and set her back to square one. The stationary is bought. The lunchbox packed. The uniform tucked in. *It's time to go to school.*

'MY DAD TOLD ME I CAN BE ANYTHING I WANT TO BE... IT WAS A VOICE THAT ECHOED IN MY HEAD WHENEVER I DOUBTED MYSELF.'

JULIE MEYER,
CEO OF ARIADNE CAPITAL.

GIRLS SHOULD STICK TO ART, MUSIC OR HOME ICT GIRLS CAN'T DO TECH. IT'S FOR BOYS. IF YOU STUDY TECH U ARE A NERD. YOU WONT B ICT PEOPLE SPEND ALL DAY IN ICT PEOPLE ARE FAT, SPOTTY AND

ECONOMICS

DARK LONELY CUBICLES.

NEVER GO OUTSIDE.

Chapter

The Vital Lesson

Our Little Miss Geek is running late. Barging past crowds of other kids, she bustles down a busy corridor just as the bell rings in her ears. Suddenly, subconsciously, something kicks in, and she begins to drag her feet...She's fourteen years old, she's at secondary school, and she's on the way to an ICT class that she doesn't want to go to. And who can blame her?

A head lies an hour in front of a computer screen, bored out of her mind by a subject she has no intention of taking further. It is at this point in our Little Miss Geek's life that all the hard work spent raising her to be comfortable with technology is thrown away. The education system should be the place where we convert childhood experiences with technology into an understanding about computing, where we lay the groundwork for a child to push on into adulthood with not only an interest in tech, but also the skills to start competing in the industry. As it is, however, we are failing our youngsters.

We are letting them go through school happy to be tech consumers, but lacking the desire to further their understanding of computing. A woefully outdated curriculum, an unappealing image and a failure to combat gender stereotypes at an early age all contribute to the fact that by the time real progress should be being made, our students – and, in particular, our girls – have long since switched off.

• •

The Image Problem

It is now, for the first time in her life, that the Little Miss Geek's image becomes incredibly important. The opinions of her classmates start to influence what she wears, how she acts and the classes she takes. Everyone around her is trying to fit in, grow up and have fun.

Most importantly, she starts to get an idea of what a girl *is supposed* to be like – and soon understands that any digression from this stereotype could lead to problems for her down the line. We have already discussed how technology has an image problem – how it is seen as the boring industry, populated by spotty men with glasses, sitting in dark rooms, bashing out numbers. It is at school where this damaging perception first takes hold.

When I recently canvassed a group of fourteen-year-old boys and girls at King Alfred School, North London, I found their ideas about the tech industry to be extremely worrying. Though many of them expressed an interest in technology – including one or two that had started to teach themselves to code – they told me that only one student out of the forty-eight in their year was taking ICT at GCSE level. When I probed them on why this was, the answers were shocking. ICT is a *soft subject*, they told me, that nobody wants on their academic record when applying for university.

The curriculum is seen as out of date and boring.

I pushed them further, and asked them to draw a picture of what they thought somebody in the I.T. industry looked like.

Most, inevitably, drew the stereotypical fat geek with glasses. What was even more interesting was that each and every one of them, boys and girls, drew a *man*.

80% of girls would like to be independent in their working environment in their ideal future job.[14]

By this age it is too late – the concept of technology being a career for women as well as men has already been lost. Why should any self-respecting young woman compromise herself by taking an interest in a subject, which public perception says isn't for her? Far better to fit to type – to pick girl-heavy classes like Art, English or a language. She will be much happier and feel less stigmatised.

She will not be considered a nerd.

The decisions we make during our school days are the first steps we take in deciding what job we will hold when we're older. The subjects we enjoy at this age are often based on where we see ourselves in ten years time.

The problem is that technology does not fit the profile of many of our young women's dream careers.

A recent study by Cisco asked UK schoolgirls which qualities they would want in their ideal future jobs.[34] One of the most popular (eighty percent of girls cited it) was the chance to be 'independent in their working environment' – something that only a third of those questioned, thought I.T. could provide.

An industry that gives the impression of letting them stretch their creative muscles, like advertising, or publishing, will also appear to allow more freedom, more individuality and

He would be old and his hair
would be overgrown because
he doesn't care what he looks like,
he only cares about computers.
Lila, 10

more independence. Another key criteria for girls found by Cisco is a job's ability to help people. Ninety percent of those surveyed said that this would play a huge part in how they would choose their future careers, but only sixty percent believed that I.T. and Computing could offer them this.[2]

Is it any wonder that girls – who don't possess the 'magnetic attraction' to computers, who don't believe that a tech career can let them help people and who draw male, sedentary geeks when asked what someone in I.T. looks like – are choosing other career paths while at school?

It would appear that our Little Miss Geeks are already looking down the road and deciding that working in technology would not meet any of their key ambitions.

We need to start listening to what girls want from their future careers and respond to their needs. The best way of fighting tech's negative image will be to show them that the industry can offer them independence, creativity, passion and philanthropy. At the moment they are not seeing these qualities, even though each of them plays a key part in any career in technology, computing or games.

Start making them more obvious and we might start seeing more girls see studying Computing as a step towards an exciting career. For now, however, it is anything but.

· ·

MYTH

TECHNOLOGY CAN'T FULFIL THE IDEALS AND AMBITIONS OF GIRLS.

FACT

IT CAN – IT'S ONE OF THE MOST CREATIVE, PHILANTHROPIC, FLEXIBLE AND TRENDY OF CAREERS.

The Curriculum Needs To Change

In 1979, psychologist and computer scientist Christopher Evans presented a six-part ITV drama entitled 'The Mighty Micro: The Impact of the Computer Revolution', which predicted the impact computing was about to have on the economy and lifestyle of the United Kingdom.[36]

This provoked the BBC into starting the first ever 'Computer Literacy Project', which aimed to teach skills such as graphics, programming, sound and artificial intelligence to the next generation, and which resulted in the creation of the famous BBC Micro – a partnership with Acorn that introduced a standardised microcomputer into schools for the first time.[37]

The Micro was a compact, relatively affordable computer that allowed users to follow the BBC's project and develop skills that would set them up for a career in an industry that most of the world hadn't even realised existed.

Looking back, it was an attitude of remarkable foresight. By putting these machines into the hands of kids – and giving them the basic skills to understand how they worked – our country paved the way for a new generation of tech-savvy employees, right as the world was demanding them.

Several women in the industry that I have spoken to over the course of researching this book – including female programmers, coders and games designers – cited the BBC Micro as hugely influential in their career choice.

Each of them said that it was invaluable having the chance to practice computing from a young age in a fun, comfortable environment. Without it they may never have developed the skills they needed to forge a life in technology. Sadly, it wasn't to last.

As computers became more integrated into our daily lives, the way we thought about them began to evolve. During the late eighties and early nineties companies like Microsoft began striving to design user-friendly interfaces that did their best to mask the complexity of what was going on inside the computer. As the number of computer users worldwide began to rocket, the move heralded the end of the era of learning how to run computers, as well as use them.

To many, a computer is just a 'magic box that runs Windows.'

Dr. Tom Crick, a Computer Science lecturer and a leader of campaigning organisation 'Computing at School' (Wales), points out the problem with having a generation of current students who have been raised on nothing more complicated than Windows 95. The majority grow up completely computer literate, but knowing nothing more about the machines they use every day.

To many, he says, a computer is just a 'magic box that runs Windows.'

This wouldn't be such an issue if the ICT curriculum hadn't gone the same way, but over the last two decades the BBC Micro – and those key computing skills it encouraged – has been replaced by the fusty school computer room. Bank after

'TO MANY STUDENTS A COMPUTER IS JUST A MAGIC BOX THAT RUNS WINDOWS.'

DR. TOM CRICK,
SENIOR LECTURER IN COMPUTER
SCIENCE AT CARDIFF METROPOLITAN
UNIVERSITY.

bank of Windows-running, bog-standard PCs, each of which are primed and ready to teach you how to use Word, Excel and Powerpoint.

As soon as computers became widely used as office tools, the way the curriculum dealt with them began to change. ICT lessons became all about giving kids the ability to make spreadsheets and write documents – valuable skills, but ones that exist in every walk of life. Just because a computer facilitates these activities, it doesn't mean that they belong in a class about technology.

You might as well spend English classes teaching kids how to hold a pencil.

In an industry that moves at lightning speed, the ICT curriculum has been painfully slow to keep up. The basic skills that are taught in an ICT lesson are already second nature to a generation of children that are born computer native – most have had to use Word or Excel independently long before they ever set foot in an ICT classroom.

One teacher we spoke to moaned that some ICT textbooks still give a breakdown of how to *back up to floppy disk*. That's the equivalent of giving kids a map that still says 'USSR', or a science book that refers to Pluto as a planet.

Though many students may enjoy the hourly respite from their more challenging classes, it means that ICT holds very little academic respect among students and parents alike –

something that has, no doubt, led to a sixty-seven percent decline in the number of students taking ICT GCSE, from 244,835 in 2004 to only 80,440 in 2011.[38]

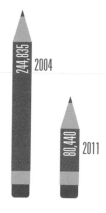

Overall students studying ICT GCSE.

The negative connotations surrounding ICT are also, by association, hurting the reputation of its more sophisticated cousin, computing.

Unlike ICT, Computer Science teaches kids the key skills they need to work with technology. The course can cover subjects like the theory of computation, algorithms, programming languages, artificial intelligence and software engineering, and is both more challenging and more academically respected. But, sadly, this doesn't make any difference. Like with ICT, our kids don't want to take it at A-Level or beyond. Since 2004 there has been a fifty-three percent reduction in overall numbers taking computing A-Level in the UK.[39]

Male students account for ninety-two percent of those taking Computer Science A-Level.

The numbers are even worse where girls are concerned. Male students account for ninety-two percent of those taking Computer Science A-Level, with this gap having widened by eight percentage points since 2004.[40] This continues when they get to university – though girls account for fifty-six percent of higher-education applicants across all subjects, they make up just fourteen percent where Computer Science and I.T. related subjects are concerned.[40]

The solution, therefore, is not simply replacing ICT with Computer Science. Though a straight swap might seem the logical choice from the point of view of the industry, it is no

'NOT WANTING TO STUDY COMPUTER SCIENCE AFTER TAKING ICT IS LIKE NOT WANTING TO DO AERONAUTICAL ENGINEERING BECAUSE YOU'VE BEEN ON AN AEROPLANE.'

DR. JUDY ROBERTSON,
SENIOR LECTURER IN COMPUTER SCIENCE
AT HERIOT-WATT UNIVERSITY.

Though girls account for 56% of higher education applicants across all subjects, they make up just fourteen percent where Computer Science and I.T. related subjects are concerned.[40]

good whatsoever unless we can make Computer Science an appealing subject. The dreaded image problem strikes again. When many kids hear the word computing they think of ICT, which means they think of spreadsheets, documents, databases, powerpoint, *zzzzzzz*.

Dr. Judy Robertson, a lecturer in the subject, says that the association between ICT and Computer Science is nonsensical: 'Not wanting to study Computer Science after taking ICT is like not wanting to do Aeronautical Engineering because you've been on an aeroplane.' How did we ever let it get this way? From having the foresight at the dawn of the modern computing era to mobilise hundreds of thousands of students to start coding in the classroom, to a time when the world is crying out for a digital workforce and we're content to let our future generation leave school with little more than basic software skills. The kids are fully aware they're being let down. The same students I spoke to at King Alfred School who described ICT as boring, expressed a huge interest in learning to code from a young age – many wish they'd been given the opportunity at school before it was too late. Sadly they are powerless to do anything about it.

Since – as we've already discussed – girls are far less likely to possess enough of a burning passion to develop computing skills in their own time, they are once again the ones who miss out most, seeing their place in the industry go to the boys who are keen enough to treat computing as a hobby outside of school.

Year Eight Is Too Late

It's all very well changing the curriculum, but if we leave it too late it will do very little good. If kids are not introduced to the basics of technology from a young age it takes a huge effort to convince them that I.T. and Computing is the subject for them. Once girls get older their minds are already made up. The social pressures of secondary school will see to that.

But get them early – before gender stereotyping and peer-pressure have really made their mark – and the process suddenly becomes a lot easier. If we can get our young girls learning basic coding and web design skills before they get to secondary school, we will go a long way to pre-emptively stamping out the idea that these things are 'boys' pastimes.'

Emma Mulqueeny is the CEO of Rewired State – a collective of developers that run regular 'Hack Days', providing task-solving research and software development for outside companies. She also runs Young Rewired State, the philanthropic arm of the company that aims to 'find and foster the young children and teenagers who are driven to teaching themselves how to code and how to programme the world around them.'[41] Mulqueeny often receives a great deal of interest from female students in the build-up to a Young Rewired State event, but finds that many of them will drop out just before it begins.

They clearly want to go along, but something stops them taking the final step. 'The problem is', she says, 'they are introduced to computing far too late in their development at a time when image and reputation has never been more important for a girl.'

If you wait until year eight to start introducing something that is potentially going to class them as geeky, and if they have to do extra homework in order to catch up with what they need to understand, you're just going to alienate ninety percent of the girls straight away. The boys don't seem to have this same need to fit in.

This led Mulqueeny to come up with the mantra 'Year Eight is Too Late' – by this point in school, she argues, technology has already lost many of our girls.

Instead she advocates introducing kids to computing at the age of nine or ten – when a child's maths and logic skills are adequate but the social pressures haven't quite kicked in. If we get them interested in studying technology before they are faced with the pressured environment of secondary school, it's her bet that the gender imbalance in I.T. and Computer Science would be dramatically reduced. As it is, however, we have a huge task to get girls interested in a subject that, in its current form, is incredibly unappealing.

'THE MAGIC AND VISION
HAVE BEEN STRIPPED AWAY
FROM I.T.'

EMER COLEMAN,
DEPUTY DIRECTOR OF DIGITAL
ENGAGEMENT,
GOVERNMENT DIGITAL SERVICE.

We Must Widen The Definition And Usage Of ICT

Every industry has drastically changed the way it operates as a result of technology. Industries that were once thought of as completely separate, such as journalism or medicine, are now intrinsically linked with the latest technological breakthroughs.

That is, every industry except education. For some reason, our school systems are yet to make this leap. It's scary how right UK Education Secretary Michael Gove was recently when he said that a Victorian schoolmaster could walk into most 21st century UK classrooms – with their rows of chairs, their boards and pens – and still feel relatively at home.[42]

Just as there is no industry that could not be improved by new technology, so too is there no subject that would not benefit from integrating itself with all the resources that modern computing can provide. Be it digital modelling in Art class or learning programming in Mathematics, as soon as we start using computers across the broader curriculum, the sooner we can start to dispel the negative connotations of 'computer only' classes.

After-school computing clubs and 'hack evenings' would also have this effect – allowing kids to develop computing skills in their own time, on their own projects, in a fun, non-academic environment. Get gadgets into their hands and get them learning how to use them.

As soon as we can get our school girls realising that computing can be applied to all parts of life and does not just have to be another boring subject, we can begin to show them the limitless potential that a career in technology can offer.

After all, our Little Miss Geek uses her computer to talk to her friends, play games, do her homework and surf the Internet. Why shouldn't she use it in all aspects of her learning as well?

● ●

The Next Step

Early 2011 saw the arrival of the NextGen report, which was commissioned by the Minister for Culture, Communications and the Creative Industries, Ed Vaizey, and undertaken by Ian Livingstone, Life President of Eidos and one of the UK's founding fathers of interactive entertainment, and Alex Hope, the co-founder of Double Negative Ltd, the UK's largest film-only VFX company.[13]

The report went into great detail about the problems facing the UK ICT curriculum and the impact that it would have on the future of the games and visual effects industries, as well as outlining the steps we need to take in order to rectify the issue. It makes for interesting reading.

The main focus of the report highlighted the disparity between the British education system – which equates ICT with office skills – and the needs of the technology and games industries that (in the case of games, especially) count for billions of pounds' worth of revenue. NextGen lobbied for – among other things – compulsory Computer Science on the curriculum, and after a struggle has finally got the attention of those who can make a difference.

After a lengthy campaign based on the report, Michael Gove, announced in January 2012 that the UK would start to follow a more flexible, forward-thinking Computer Science and ICT programme, part of which would be developed in partnership with universities and businesses. Schools and teachers, he promised, would no longer be bound by an outdated, micromanaged curriculum but would have the freedom to teach material they thought relevant, using the resources at their disposal.

It's a bold approach, but if it pays off it could be the key to rehabilitating ICT and ridding it of its boring, unacademic associations – as well as rescuing a potentially lost generation of talented computer scientists.

There may also be hope in finding a successor to the BBC Micro, which played such a pivotal part in British education's previous technological revolution. The Raspberry Pi is a tiny circuit board that costs around £25, which, when plugged into a keyboard and a TV, becomes a general-purpose computer running Linux.[44] A philanthropic project that started in Cambridge, the creators of the Raspberry Pi wanted to provide the same thing that the good old Micro did back in the eighties – an affordable, simple way of getting teachers and students programming in the classroom and at home. The hope is that the low price of the unit will break the absurd economic cycle of computer equipment that forces schools to keep using ten-year-old equipment because they are unable to afford the latest model.

Entrepreneur David Braben, a trustee of Raspberry Pi, says that their aim is to bring an association between computers and creativity back into schools: 'The school ICT curriculum is so far away from creativity. The computer is no longer seen as a creative device. It is seen as a glorified typewriter.'

Without tools like the Pi, he believes, the full potential of the computer will remain elusive – and scary – for our students. 'There is a lot of techno fear as people don't have an understanding of what is inside a computer. We need to look under the bonnet and take the fear out of technology.'

Thankfully it looks like they have a great chance of success – when it launched in March 2012, the first model sold out in minutes.

The desire to learn is clearly there, and projects like this show how simple it is to provide the tools for our next generation of technology employees. Major technology companies should start developing similar ideas.

With a more up-to-date and exciting curriculum on the horizon, and programming tools like the Raspberry Pi finding their way into the hands of schoolgirls, it's possible that maybe, just maybe, our Little Miss Geek might soon find herself enjoying her Computer lessons.

• •

Moving From STEM to STEAM

That is, of course, if she ends up taking them for long enough. Significant gender gaps still exist between Maths and Science subjects – favoured heavily by boys – and creative subjects, like English or Art, which are favoured by girls.

One of the key principles that the NextGen report advocated is what Livingstone has described as moving away from the concept of traditional STEM subjects and careers and thinking of them as STEAM – Science, Technology, Engineering, Arts and Mathematics. In his 2011 Mactaggart lecture Google Executive Chairman Eric Schmidt made the following observation regarding one of the major problems facing the UK technology industry:[45]

You need to bring art and science back together. Think back to the glory days of the Victorian era. It was a time when the same people wrote poetry and built bridges. Lewis Carroll didn't just write one of the classic fairy tales of all time, he was also a Mathematics tutor at Oxford… There's been a drift to the humanities – Engineering and Science aren't championed. Even worse, both sides seem to denigrate the other - to use what I'm told is the local vernacular, you're either a 'luvvy' or a 'boffin'.

Schmidt's outsider's eye nails a problem that has long bothered the UK – the divide between creativity and science in our schools. We are no longer encouraged to be polymaths, and instead are forced to choose between one field or the other.

MYTH

YOU ARE EITHER A 'LUVVY' OR A 'BOFFIN'.

FACT

TECHNOLOGY AND ART CAN GO HAND IN HAND.

Da Vinci was one of the greatest painters who ever lived. He was also one of the greatest inventors. If he was at a British school today he would have been forced to be one or the other.

This distinction is partly the result of the way our university system is organised, unlike in many other countries (including the US), students cannot take multiple subjects and must focus on a single strand. This approach has its merits, but does force kids at school to pigeon-hole themselves at an increasingly early age. The competition for places at university means our students can no longer hedge their bets – mixed A-levels are feared as signalling indecisiveness, and so a complementary cocktail of subjects is devised. Want to take English at uni? You should drop Physics as soon as you can. Going to be an engineer? Well what do you need to take French for!

In limiting ourselves to this creative/scientific division we hurt our chances of not only becoming more well-rounded people, but also of exploring the myriad of opportunities that are available to a graduate in the working world. We cut ourselves off from countless jobs we might thrive in, all because we are pushed into deciding: 'yes, I'm an arts person'. What makes the situation so ironic is that – as I've already mentioned – technology is one of the most creative industries an intelligent young woman could join, and it is in dire need of fresh brains that can imagine as well as deduct.

Mark Hardisty knows a thing or two about trying to show off how creative I.T. can be. A sixth form ICT teacher, he is also the founder of Games Britannia, an annual schools video games festival that aims to show kids what the games industry has to offer them. Over the past few years Games Britannia has grown from a one-school project to a national, three-day event, featuring high profile speakers from across all sectors of the industry. It has proved immensely popular, showing that the desire to learn more about technology is clearly there when offered – it's just that day-to-day, students don't get the opportunity to experience what a job in an industry like games could offer them.

Hardisty says Games Britannia is aiming to push the move from STEM to STEAM: 'It's all about bringing kids in who are good at art, bringing kids in that are good at music, bringing kids in that are good at writing.' This approach, he says, will probably do wonders for making the industry more appealing to girls. But it's not just for their benefit. The games industry, he says, needs creative skills desperately. 'For all the will in the world, you can be the best programmer around but it still doesn't mean you can make a good game.'

A game, like a film, is an incredibly rich product, with a story, dialogue, cinematography, artwork and a soundtrack that all play just as vital a part in its finished state as the code and the engine that makes it run. The comparison between games and films is an interesting one. Both are huge, multi-billion dollar entertainment industries. Both employ a workforce that is part artist/part technical. Both reach millions of people, every day. Yet Hollywood – and everything it represents – remains a dream career choice for many school-kids. Our Little Miss Geek would probably dream about going into the movies. She's very unlikely to dream about the video game industry.

It's all about profile. Despite its enormous size, the games industry is still regarded as niche while the film industry places itself at the centre of popular culture. Why is it that school kids know the names of famous film directors but they don't know the names of games designers, even if their games have sold far more than most films?

The film industry is simply more visible. It has never been afraid to let aspiring young creatives peek behind the curtain, to show them the magicians who make the magic, and make heroes out of them. The games industry is yet to make this sort of breakthrough. Ian Livingstone maintains that this is because it's still a comparatively new art form.

Film and music have been around for a long long time. If you think about it in terms of film, the games industry is essentially in the 1920s. It's very much still misunderstood by the establishment.

How long do we have to wait before games and technology become accepted as mainstream, exciting career prospects? Thirty years? Forty?

While we won't be able to match the mass appeal of music or film quite yet, there are steps we can take right now to make games and technology a much more appealing place to be. We need to finally put the image of the nerd to bed.

'THE COMPUTER IS NO LONGER SEEN AS A CREATIVE DEVICE. IT IS SEEN AS A GLORIFIED TYPEWRITER.'

DAVID BRABEN,
CHAIRMAN, FRONTIER
DEVELOPMENTS.

Show Kids Our People

So how do we go about this? We know from the inside that tech can be one of the most exciting places a person can work, with some of the most inspiring, creative employees around. But that perception isn't transferring to our schools.

For most kids, technology is something that is made behind a dark curtain. They are all very aware of the products that come out at the end, but have no idea about what the people involved actually do.

We can't just tell them what they're missing – they won't believe us. We need to show them.

We need to show them the passion. We need to show them the creativity. We need to show them the variety of exciting opportunities that await any talented, hardworking student.

The only way to combat the outdated stereotype of technology being a boring career choice is to give kids tangible examples to the contrary. Let's make our most exciting industry people visible in schools. Be it through outreach programmes, workshops or competitions, let's put a face to the industry and give them a taste of what a life in technology might be like.

It's particularly important to show schoolgirls that there are women doing great work as well as men. Since the majority of role models for girls tend to be female,[13] is it any wonder they give no thought to following a tech career when a great many of them will have never met a woman working in technology?

It's time for them to come out from behind the curtain and show our Little Miss Geek that they're not all a bunch of antisocial nerds. If she believes us, she might just have a shot. If we're going to move forward, the following things need to happen:

1 We need to change the curriculum and teach cutting-edge Computer Science and not dull ICT.

2 We need to get kids learning about computers at a young age, before girls are affected by social pressures.

3 We need to change the image of the industry in the eyes of our children – make it seem fun and appealing, not boring and nerdy.

Once these changes are in place our Little Miss Geek might just start taking an interest. She might even start to thrive at computing, take it further and end up with a job at the heart of the technology industry. Problem solved. End of story.

Right? Well, not exactly...

STAGE 4

STAY IN THE INDUSTRY

difficulty very hard

TECH BUSINESS

Chapter

Same Industry, New Image

* * *

We've done it. She's there! Our Little Miss Geek is all grown up, suited and booted and on the way to the offices of an up and coming technology business. She's fought her way into an industry where her gender is criminally under-represented, and has launched herself into the initial stages of a potentially incredible and exciting career.

* * *

Pop the champagne. Pass round the cake. We did it. We got her there! Except, sadly, that is not the end of her story. It's not enough getting her into the technology industry – we have to keep her there. We must make tech a great place for a working woman. Unfortunately, right now, there is still a great deal of work to be done. Technology remains a man's world that women still struggle to succeed in.

Pink It And Shrink It? Please...

So why is tech such a tough place to be a woman? To be honest, many tech companies don't help themselves when it comes to dispelling the 'boys' club' myth. The way an industry markets products to its customer base speaks volumes about its attitudes. It reveals what they think their customers like and how they think their customers act.

Pink It and Shrink It – the crude formula companies use for 'female products'.

So when a company markets a product aimed specifically at women, it tells us a great deal about the way women are perceived within the boardroom. This is where the technology industry reveals its shortcomings. For years they have been peddling what Lady Geek calls the 'Pink It and Shrink It' approach. It's a crude formula: take a standard tech product and make it smaller *(for tiny women's hands!)*; make it less complicated *(for tiny women's brains!)*; and slap some pink sparkly bits on it *(because all girls love pink!)*. Voilà! You have now made a gadget fit for a woman. It doesn't matter that it's usually nowhere near as powerful as gadgets aimed at men – women don't care about that sort of thing. They just want it to look pretty, right? The mobile phone industry is the worst offender. For years it has pushed handsets at women by taking entry-level models, giving them a tacky pink paint job and garnishing the whole affair with some useless accessories. It was hoped that this nonsense attitude would die out with the emergence of the smartphone market, but sadly little has changed.

As recently as late 2011, HTC released the Rhyme – its latest model aimed at women. Every cliché was present and correct:

the dainty size, the underwhelming specs, the pink colour (OK, so it was purple…). But HTC's worst offence was a 'special addition': flashing, vibrating 'charm' on a cord attached to the handset that was designed to make the phone easier to take out of a bag. Because women were having so much trouble operating normal phones, obviously. *And of course, they love accessories…*

Boys' club.

The fact that year on year, respectable tech companies like HTC continue to persevere with these outdated ideas highlights their lack of understanding of modern women.

> Why on earth would any woman want to work in an industry that continues to patronise her?

Even worse than these archaic marketing approaches is the 'boys' club' misogyny that has somehow become ingrained in parts of the industry. The attitude that means technology conferences are still populated by scantily clad 'booth babes' who are in charge of displaying products but know next to nothing about the tech behind them. The attitude that saw tech giant ASUS tweet a picture of a pretty woman standing next to the back of one of their computers, with the tag: 'The rear looks pretty nice. So does the new Transformer AIO.'[46]

Eugh. That this sort of crass, misguided comment is being posted via the official mouthpiece of a major company shows exactly why the tech industry has to change before it can offer a working environment that women want to be a part of. The industry must purge itself completely of these attitudes

'IN MY EXPERIENCE, MOST WOMEN TEND TO ONLY FEEL COMFORTABLE APPLYING FOR A NEW JOB IF THEY HAVE A 100% SKILL MEN ARE MORE LIKELY TO PUT THEMSELVES FORWARD IF THEY ONLY FULFIL HALF OF THE JOB REQUIREMENTS'

MAGGIE BERRY,
MD OF WOMEN IN TECHNOLOGY.

in order to change. But I'm well aware that it's useless me shouting 'we need to make technology a better industry for women!' without suggesting how that might be achieved.

So what's the solution?

We need to promote long-term measures that will change attitudes from the boardroom to the factory floor. It's all very well pointing out all of the things that make the technology industry an inhospitable place for women – but in the long term that will get us nowhere. The last thing I want to do is set women against the industry. If we are going to make any progress we need to move forward together, as one.

Transforming the tech industry's gender imbalance is about improving companies on three counts:

• •

1 How to Engage the Next Generation of Brilliant Women.

2 How to Retain the Brilliant Women you already have.

3 How to get more Brilliant Women in the Boardroom.

• •

There's no point bitching and moaning. It's time to take action.

• •

HOW TO ENGAGE THE NEXT GENERATION OF BRILLIANT WOMEN

1. SHOW OFF TECH'S HEROINES.

2. WIDEN THE DEFINITION OF TECH.

3. MAKE IT REAL.

1. Show Off Tech's Heroines.

Despite the fact that men dominate the industry, there are still thousands of incredible women working for technology companies all over the world. The problem is, you very rarely hear from them.

Give women a voice.

Mark Hardisty from Games Britannia believes that changing this holds the key to getting girls interested in tech: 'the role models are out there for young women if you look hard enough. If we can get these women front and centre it will be much easier to attract more girls into tech.' Research confirms this opinion; Catalyst has found that the most common career barrier cited by women in tech was: 'a lack of role models in the company who are similar to me.' [47]

Aspiration is all about projection – one has to be able to picture oneself achieving something if one is going to stand a chance of achieving it. Without strong role models to look up to, girls won't be able to picture themselves working in the tech industry. The solution is simple: if we want more girls to aspire to working in tech we need to start making more of the amazing women already doing so. Put them, as Hardisty says, 'front and centre'. Show them off. Give them a voice.

The power of recommendation is an incredible thing. Social media has meant we are more connected than ever, and the female network has never been stronger. A woman will be attracted to a company if she sees another impressive woman tweeting, blogging and talking about working for that company. Word spreads fast – we should let the women in our companies spread it. If we let the unspoken heroines of our organisations tell their story we'll be amazed at the positive results. If we tap into the current female network successfully, we can use it to reach out to and recruit the next generation of female talent.

2. Widen The Definition Of Tech.

It's no secret that the technology industry can be a little narrow minded, and I've spoken a great deal about how the 'magnetic attraction' can feel like a must-have attribute for anyone wanting to work in the technology industry. The idea still remains that if you want to work with tech, you have to really love tech. All this makes the industry seem like a bit of an exclusive club. There's a feeling that you have to be seriously switched on, plugged in and know your C from your C++ in order to get through the door – let alone get ahead. This adult extension of the 'magnetic attraction' not only alienates many of the best graduates, it often makes current employees feel unwelcome and ill-equipped.

Ann Charles is a project manager at a broadcast and media company in charge of rolling out a new radio broadcast software across the entire organisation. She moved from a creative role in producing to a technical role in the broadcast engineering projects department. The transition was not nearly as hard as she had expected given the complicated terminology and criteria that had been attached to her new role. Over complicating matters is driving away great employees, she says: 'Nonsense terminology alienates people - it makes these jobs seem alien, when in reality most people can do them. It's all about confidence. It's about encouraging people to use the skill set they have.'

"74X3 443 70 j0l_ll2 _134l)3l2!"

'Nonsense terminology alienates people – it makes these jobs seem alien, when in reality most people can do them.'

Even though women like Charles are perfectly capable of doing a technology job, they remain much less likely than men to apply. Stats from Intellect show that ninety percent of women in the technology industry will only feel comfortable applying for a job where they match almost all of the criteria. [48]

It's all very reminiscent of how the 'magnetic attraction' is freezing schoolgirls out of the ICT classroom. Overly-specific criteria forces women to think: 'If a job needs someone as specific as that, then they are definitely not looking for somebody like me'. But the industry doesn't just need super-geeks – it needs all-rounders. We need to make it so that the best graduates in English, History, Economics, and Law as well as Maths and Computer Science begin to see technology companies as not only a legitimate employment option, but also an exciting one. To do this we have to open up the gates and not be so precious with our golden tickets to the chocolate factory.

STEM subjects are dominated by men, so giving more opportunities to talented, intelligent, non-STEM graduates would give more women an opportunity to break into the industry. The financial sector has done it for years, using graduate schemes that value personal aptitude as much as

'WE **NEED** TO FIND MORE FEMALE ROLE MODELS. FIND THE ROCKSTARS OF OUR INDUSTRY TO **BECOME OUR AMBASSADORS.**'

DR. JO TWIST,
CEO, UKIE.

specific knowledge to hoover up the most ambitious and talented young employees around – whatever their specialty. How many brand new Deloitte or PWC employees have an in-depth knowledge of corporate accounting or tax policy before joining? After a few months on the job that ceases to matter.

If we want our technology companies to be bursting at the seams with the best young graduates – male and female – we have to stop looking for fully formed computer geniuses and start developing recruitment schemes that identify and nurture potential talent. Do this and we'll not only see a broader skill-range amongst employees, but also more diversity. Let's broaden our definitions of I.T., start recruiting from a diverse pool and let the technology industry reap the benefits.

3. Make It Real.

It's inevitable that there is an air of secrecy about the technology industry. When so much of a company's success depends on getting one over on its competitors and getting a new product to market before anybody else, the tricks of the trade are bound to be closely guarded. But this lack of visibility has a drawback – it means potential employees have no idea what actually goes on behind tech's doors.

Most girls would be able to make a good attempt at guessing what goes on inside a PR or advertising agency – but how much would they know about a technology company? Maggie Philbin, the much-loved presenter of BBC Science programme 'Tomorrow's World', and the founder of Teen Tech – an inspiring engineering and technology event for teenagers – believes that the more we keep technology behind a veil, the less we give girls to aspire to: 'We need to give girls something concrete to dream about' she says. 'Girls need to touch, feel and taste what a career in technology and the games industry is like'.

She's absolutely right. Without having an idea of what the industry is like, why would anybody want to work there? We need to start showing girls what they could be doing on a day-to-day basis at the most vibrant, exciting parts of our companies. Technology is an industry bursting with variety. There are thousands of different jobs, suited to a whole range of skill-sets. Let's introduce short-term apprenticeship programmes at the heart of companies that give the employee a taste of working in different departments at our companies. That way they are more likely to discover where their talents are best suited – and more likely to come back for more.

Be it through giving talented students job opportunities in their holidays, or running sponsorship schemes to help them with their tuition fees, we need to make a huge effort to connect with young women making their first career decisions.

Draw back the veil and give them the chance to see what's on offer – and let them show you what they can do while they're at it.

1. take last years brand new device for men

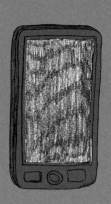

2. pink it

3. shrink it

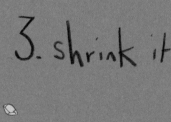

release additional premium sparkly model edition

(for women, by men)

HOW TO RETAIN
THE BRILLIANT WOMEN
YOU ALREADY HAVE

1 EMBRACE FEMININITY.

2 TALK OPENLY ABOUT THE GENDER ISSUE.

3 GET SYSTEMIZERS AND EMPATHIZERS
TALKING EACH OTHER'S LANGUAGE.

1. Embrace Femininity.

The technology trade association Intellect has found that forty-seven percent of women in technology believe that they have to act like a man to get ahead.[49] Any industry that makes a talented woman feel like she has to hide her true self to do well is going to have a real struggle on its hands to keep her on the books.

47% percent of women in technology believe that they have to act like a man to get ahead.

Women should no longer have to feel like they need to put on a 'male suit'. The workplace is a place for everybody – there should be no such thing as a 'male office' in any line of work, let alone one that makes products that are used as much by women as they are by men. Several women I know in the industry are much more comfortable considering themselves 'one of the boys' – matching their male colleagues blow for blow on their own turf.

Except it's not their turf. It's everyone's turf.

There is no reason why a modern working woman should feel like she has to be more masculine and draw attention away from the fact that she's a woman. To do that would be to muzzle some of the qualities that make her a valuable asset.

Lee Epting is the former Global Content Services Director at Vodafone. After starting her career in mortgage lending, she landed a job with a telecommunications company and hasn't looked back during a long successful career in technology. Unlike many women I have spoken to, however, putting on the 'male suit' is not something Epting believes in doing.

This attitude is incredibly refreshing, and one that the technology industry should embrace. As long as women feel like they have to act like men they will only feel half at home – and will only give you half of themselves.

For me the strength that a woman has is her femininity. I have often found that being a women has given me the opportunity for growth – I find I can get better airtime as a woman because I am often unique in the room. I think we should celebrate the uniqueness – tech can benefit from the more emotional approach that women can bring.

We need to make tech a place where women aren't afraid to be women – where they are celebrated for their femininity.

2. Talk Openly About The Gender Issue.

Why is it that when we see an attractive young woman, the last thing we might expect is that she's good at programming? Remember the children that drew the fat, bespectacled man when asked what a person in I.T. looks like? The same perception exists in I.T. itself.

The industry still remains uncomfortable with women in technical roles, with stats showing that they are often pushed into so-called 'softer skills' roles – such as management, marketing and PR – as they climb further up the ladder.[50]

Kate Craig-Wood says that following her transsexual transition she found that the more attractive she became the less men assumed she knew about technology. Craig-Wood has years of experience, learnt to code at the age of nine and

'THE MORE ATTRACTIVE
I BECAME THE LESS MEN
ASSUMED I KNEW ABOUT
TECHNOLOGY.'

KATE CRAIG-WOOD,
CO-FOUNDER OF MEMSET.

runs a hugely successful technology business. But as soon as her appearance changed, the assumptions others made about her skill-level changed as well.

It's an incredibly harmful attitude. No one should have to constantly prove themselves in any situation, especially when they possess skills that could make a valuable contribution to the industry. But for some reason we never talk about the issue at work. The problem feels unmentionable. Many women – including myself – find it tough to talk about gender discrimination because we fear that by drawing attention to it we might perpetuate the situation.

At one of my previous jobs I found myself hugely outnumbered by men. Men populated the offices and the boardrooms, and there was a heightened 'old boys' club' mentality. Looking back, it made it an incredibly uncomfortable place for myself and the few other women working there, and slowly over time I found myself shrinking in confidence. My voice became increasingly muted and I kept questioning my actions and myself. Why was I not being heard? What was I doing wrong? I felt like a fish out of water.

What made things worse was that I felt unable to discuss the situation with anyone. I couldn't tell my boss how I felt as I was unsure how to bring it up and had no idea what his reaction would be. No one had ever said anything before and so, mistakenly, I felt like I should follow suit. If only I'd felt comfortable enough to speak up.

Admitting that there is a problem can often feel like admitting defeat, but leaving it unspoken means that nothing will ever change.

It's like sweeping rubbish under the carpet – you can forget about it in the short term, but eventually things start to rot. But the only way to kill off stereotypes is by raising awareness. Tech companies should talk to their employees – male and female – about the negative perception of women. We must no longer leave these things unsaid. Half the time stereotyping is so embedded in our culture that we can be ignorant of the effect it is having on our attitudes and opinions. As soon as we become a little more aware of discrimination – however accidental – we all become better placed to take measures to avoid it.

Most importantly, let's give female employees the chance to express themselves. Give them a platform to express how they feel about being in the minority: do they believe there is a damaging, overtly 'male culture' at their company? Fundamentally, let's ask all our employees what we can do to make their workplace a more female friendly place and get some perspective on what needs to be done.

3. Get Systemizers And Empathizers Talking Each Other's Language.

In the second chapter, I wrote about Simon Baron-Cohen and his 'E-S theory'.[51] The difference between the 'male brain', which Baron-Cohen classifies as a systemizer (good at understanding and building systems) and the empathizing

Get systemizers and empathizers talking each others' language.

'female brain' (which is much better at reading emotions and responding to them) may go some way to explaining why women – who are more likely to possess the 'female brain' type – feel uncomfortable in the tech industry.

But every industry needs both types to work together – and technology is no different. Tech is in desperate need of as many good empathizers as it is systemizers. So much of technology is to do with how we interact with each other and the world around us. It's about how we talk and how we play, and it needs creative, empathetic types as much as it needs those with brains made for building and programming. Most importantly, however, it needs both types to work together.

Companies need empathizers – so make them feel welcome. Make sure that their valuable skills are appreciated and encouraged as much as their systemizing colleagues. If empathizers feel out of place in your business, businesses will cease to be a hotbed of ideas, and stagnate.

But equally, companies need systemizers, and we must train those of a more empathetic persuasion to adapt their working style and understand a systematic approach. Lady Geek recently ran a series of Female Immersion Workshops for a large mobile operator in South Africa with the aim of helping transform the way they sell to women. Helpfully for us, the senior team we were working with told us that the employees we would be speaking to were largely 'systemizers.' Because we knew this upfront, we adapted our style to present the information in a very systematic way, using scorecards and a quantitative methodology. As a team of empathizers, it was very important that in order to change their mindset, we adapted to the systemizer mentality.

We need to identify the empathizers and systemizers in tech organisations and help them learn to speak each other's language. Once empathizers are accommodated and made to feel as valued as systemizers, more women will start to see a technology company as a place where they can flourish.

• •

HOW TO GET MORE BRILLIANT WOMEN IN THE BOARDROOM

1. MAKE TECH A GREAT PLACE TO BE A MUM.

2. EMPOWER AND MENTOR WOMEN.

3. GIVE WOMEN A LADDER TO CLIMB.

1. Make Tech A Great Place To Be A Mum.

So what happens if our Little Miss Geek (now a full-grown Lady Geek) decides to have children? How child friendly are the tech and games industry?

The time when women are most likely to start having children – late twenties and early thirties – is a key period in their careers. It's the time when the inexperienced salad days of that first job have been left behind and some real career traction is starting to be made. Maternity leave often threatens to derail this progress, especially when workers are not encouraged to return after an extended absence.

When surveyed by Intellect, an incredible eighty-four percent of women working in technology said that more needed to be done to encourage those on maternity leave to return to their careers.[52] Companies that don't do enough to hold on to new mothers are giving away valuable human resources – every woman who doesn't return to her post after taking maternity leave represents years of discarded training and experience.

84% of women working in technology said that more needed to be done to encourage those on maternity leave to return to their careers.[52]

Add that to the fact that the average cost of recruiting a new employee in the UK has been estimated at £5,311, and you can see how little sense it makes to let talented employees slip away.[53] New motherhood can be an incredibly stressful and overwhelming time. The more that companies can do to ease the stress and make coming back to work an option that is both viable and attractive, the more they will be able to hold on to the talented women in their ranks.

I remember when I returned from maternity leave and was expected to hide my 'other life' from my peers. We were not encouraged to speak about what it felt like to be working mums.

We were not encouraged to have photos on our desks and share stories of our little ones. I've always been someone that likes to bring a bit of my personality into the office, so to be made to feel like I had to bury such an important part of myself was devastating. Tech companies need to start doing more to support new parents. Why not prepare take-away meals for their family so they don't have to worry about the dinner rush – a wonderful scheme piloted with great success in Egypt by Vodafone. Give them a 'maternity buddy' to help share their experiences and let them know that they are not the only person going through their situation. [54]

Let's launch 'Mum Returner' schemes for those mums who have taken a few years out and, now that their children are bigger, want to re-enter the workforce. Let's make it possible for mums to ease back in, working flexibly for the first few months. Confidence can be lost so we need to ensure that tech companies not only encourage mums back to work but offer them support and provide mentors when they re-enter the business.

2. Empower & Mentor Women.

A company is never going to encourage a new wave of women to join their ranks if they can't hold on to those that it currently employ. Efforts must be made to ensure that female employees feel well looked after. It's vital in any industry to make an employee – male or female – feel like he/she is working from a position of strength. Creating a female network within your company can do wonders for achieving this effect for women.

77% of companies reported that mentoring programmes were effective in increasing employee retention.[56]

Many of those who I have spoken to felt that the absence of other women around them meant they had to work doubly hard to get ahead. We need to make sure the women in our industry feel they are not alone. When polled by Catalyst, one of the most common career barriers cited by women in technology was as follows:

'Not having a mentor, sponsor or champion who makes my accomplishments known to important people in the company.'[55]

Any tech company looking to increase the aspirations of its female employees should – if it hasn't already – introduce a mentoring programme. Give talented employees contact time with those in more senior positions who are most similar to them. Let women see and interact with other women who have already climbed the ladder.

35% percent of employees who do not receive regular mentoring look for another job within twelve months.[57]

Research has shown how effective a mentoring programme can be. One study showed that seventy-seven percent of companies reported that mentoring programmes were effective in increasing employee retention,[56] while another found that thirty-five percent of employees who do not receive regular mentoring look for another job within twelve

61% of games had more than ten years experience in the sector.

months.[6] Few women like to feel like a lone wolf. Having the reassurance of knowing somebody is looking out for you at work is one of the most valuable career assets a person can have. We all need support.

We need to amplify women's voices and ensure they are heard.

3. Give Women A Ladder To Climb.

Much of this book has been focused on one key fact – that women currently hold only seventeen percent of jobs in the technology sector. But I am yet to talk about that seventeen percent themselves. Who are they? How are they treated? And what are their chances of success having been one of the lucky ones to break through?

Only 26% of women had reached senior management or board level. [13]

In a survey conducted by Women In Technology along with Intellect, an attempt was made to deduce the speed of career progression for women in the technology industry. Of all the women that were interviewed, sixty-one percent had more than ten years experience in the sector – yet only twenty-six percent of those had reached senior management or board level.[58]

Most women, the survey found, got stuck at junior or mid-level management, with many of those who had not made the leap up saying that they were being passed over for promotion in favour of men. These findings are confirmed in a report conducted by Catalyst in 2008, which found that women with higher levels of qualification – masters degrees and above – were more likely to perceive barriers to career advancement than those less qualified. The report concluded this was because they were more likely to be higher up in corporations and therefore more likely to hit the glass ceiling.[59]

Why would any talented woman stick around in an industry that is not going to reward her hard work? Nobody likes stagnating – we must give women a ladder to climb.

Research from the Anita Borg Institute shows that when women do climb the ladder to the highest level, they are often put in far more precarious positions than their male counterparts. A senior woman is far more likely to inherit a team or an organisation in crisis – and thus far more likely to not last as long in her position.[60] This phenomena is what's often referred to as a glass cliff – when we do let them get there, we don't let them last long before we push them off the edge.

We need to protect our talented women. Don't throw them to the wolves – give them the chance to prove themselves at the top of your company in an environment that is about building on success rather than fire fighting. None of this will make any difference at all however, unless we can achieve the most important task of all.

The Ultimate Goal
– Make Tech Glamorous And Desirable

And so we come to the problem that has haunted our Little Miss Geek from birth, through school and right into the industry. One that has dissuaded her – and her peers – from embracing technology from the ICT classroom to the careers fair.

One that, if we work hard enough, we can overcome. The image problem. The negative idea of the 'geek'. We cry and moan about how unfair it is that all tech workers are labelled nerds, but then we don't do anything to dispel the myth. If people continue to believe that the tech industry is boring it's because we're not showing them otherwise.

If tech has an image problem we need to project a new image. The industry needs to stop hiding its wonderful people behind its products. We need to show off the talent, the character and the creativity that exists within the walls of every tech company from the smallest start-up to the biggest multi-national. As long as there are no faces to technology companies, as long as their identity is defined solely by the things they create and not by the people that create them, they will seem faceless and inaccessible to those on the outside.

So tech companies: show your employees off. Make them look good. Dare I say it – make them look cool. Put them front and centre alongside all the amazing products they invent. Make the connection between the tablet and the person who designs it.

Show that designing games can be just as fun as playing them. Don't hide your employees behind the curtain – put them on the stage or the corporate blog. Start running adverts that show off your workers. Start getting more magazines and newspapers to profile you. Start hosting class trips to your offices and labs.

If everyone working in the tech industry gave up one working day of their time we could kill off the image problem once and for all. They could go into a school and give a talk. They could write a blog. They could have a one-to-one chat with a child they know. It doesn't matter – just so long as they pick a day and give it over to getting the next generation enthused about technology. If we truly want to get the next generation excited about the industry, we need to get to a place where our designers are as well known as our products.

The next Sir Jonathan Ive should be as famous as Stella McCartney.

Get enough faces out there and with any luck we might kill off the 'tech equals nerd' image once and for all. We've got a long road ahead of us, but I have no doubt that a new day is coming. We can change things from the top down and the inside out. Starting at the very heart of our companies and working outwards, the time has come to change the way a woman's relationship with technology is treated from the cradle to the boardroom. If we take action now it won't be long until our Little Miss Geek is free to realise her potential, tackle technology and maybe, just maybe, *change the world.*

5

Conclusion

Her face is ecstatic as she leaves the Palace, clutching her gong. She poses for the photographs, shakes hand after hand and embraces her family. 'For services to the technology industry, Dame...'. She is a game changer. An industry leader. A pioneer. The Little Miss Geek is all grown up.

It's a wonderful image that I hope we will soon start to see more off. Currently only seventeen percent of jobs in the UK technology sector are held by women.[1] We should not rest until that figure reaches fifty percent; if we all work together this should be completely achievable. In order to do this we must think big; we need to tackle the whole issue – not just within the industry, but in universities, at school-level and even in the way we raise our little girls. We need to make our industry a great place for a woman to work. We need to make our schools a place where technology and computing seem exciting, not dreary. Above all, we need to raise our little girls to believe that science and technology are not the preserve of the boys in the playground.

Currently only 17% of jobs in the UK tech sector are held by women.[1] We should not rest until that figure reaches 50%.

Men and women are different – of that there is no doubt – but we have seen through the course of this book how those differences are a cause for celebration. Not all boys are scientists. Not all girls are artists. Both have a role to play in the future of the technology industry.

There is no reason why women shouldn't be working alongside men, and all of the old excuses – that they aren't born with the right skills; that they are derailed by motherhood; that they simply aren't interested – should now be put to bed. Old stereotypes and prejudices must be retired once and for all if we're going to move forward.

But that won't be enough on its own. We also need to work harder than ever before, taking immediate, active steps to change the situation. It can be done, but we have to act quickly before the situation gets even worse.

Most pressingly we need to change the image of the industry in the eyes of the next generation. Remember those pictures the primary school children drew? The army of fat, bespectacled men? The hope is that – with our help – the age of the nerd is finally coming to an end. With that in mind, here is the Lady Geek manifesto – *10 specific initiatives that any technology company could set up immediately in order to improve the way they recruit, retain and inspire female talent.*

These ideas are achievable and actionable and are designed to yield tangible benefits in a short period of time.

Each of these tasks on its own is perfectly doable and each, if implemented correctly, will make a big difference to overcoming technology's gender gap. We are working with large corporates to make this happen.

If we can achieve all of them simultaneously, we will not only halt the decline of women going into the industry, but spur on an increase that will set us well on the way to achieving gender equality in the tech industry.

• •

THE LADY GEEK MANIFESTO

1. APPRENTICESHIPS

2. MUM RETURNER SCHEME

3. SCHOOL MENTORSHIP PROGRAMME

4. FEMALE SPONSOR PROGRAMME

5. BURSARY SCHEME

6. FEMALE EMPLOYER BRAND CAMPAIGN

7. TECH SKILLS REQUIREMENT AUDIT

8. FEMALE HEROES PROGRAMME

9. INVEST IN FEMALE START-UPS

10. LEARN TO 'CODE IN A DAY' WORKSHOPS

1. Offer Apprenticeships Schemes For Girls Aged 16-21.

Your next star developer or designer might not come from a traditional academic background. Let's focus not just on technology students, but on other talented young individuals from any background. It's going to be more important than ever to recognise raw talent, and develop it within the company. Apprenticeships are one of the easiest ways for corporate leaders to recruit a more diverse workforce.

Benefit to Employers: Reduce your recruitment fees and bring a more diverse talent pool that you can nurture to fit the company needs.

2. Bring In 'Mum Returner' Recruitment Schemes.

We must not only focus on young women but also on women who have left the industry. Forty-one percent of women leave technology companies after 10 years of experience, compared to only seventeen percent of men[61] – it is an easy win to focus on those brilliant women who left the industry either from disillusionment or after having children for a career break. Let's give mums a new inspiring environment and get their career path back on track. The most successful 'Mum-Returner' schemes pair new returnees with mums who returned in previous years and support them during the first 6 months of their return.

41% of women leave tech companies after 10 years of experience, compared to only 17% of men.[60]

Benefit to Employers: Far more cost-effective to re-recruit 'Mum Returners' than new talent. It is also a great way for you to show other mums in your company that you are committed to them.

3. School Mentorship Programme.

Encourage your technical staff to devote one day a year to going into schools and giving careers advice. If we spread the workload we can maximise all the incredible talent we have at our disposal to show every Little Miss Geek out there what they can gain by taking an interest in tech. Even if it sparks an interest in only 1% of school leavers, it will be worth it.

Benefit to Employers: Build your future talent pool and demonstrate to your employees your commitment to building the future of the industry.

4. Female Sponsorship Programme.

Fortune 500 firms that put women at the top were 44% more profitable than the median companies in their industries.[62]

Anecdotal research has shown us while women are helped greatly by mentors, a *sponsor* is more beneficial. A mentor will give women advice along the way, but a sponsor will help women negotiate a pay raise, give women a voice at the top table and will help carve out the 'ladder' for women to make it to the top. Make sure each of your top female talent has an identified sponsor in your business, and show that your company has a commitment to helping women smash through the glass-ceiling.

Benefit to Employers: Fortune 500 firms with the best records of putting women at the top were on average 44% more profitable than the median companies in their industries.[62] It can only benefit your company if the right women are at your top table.

5. Offer Bursary Schemes That Help Fund Talented Girls Through University In Return For A Two-Year Placement.

If we make these jobs seem like tangible opportunities with

tangible rewards, we can get girls to seriously consider a career in tech. This approach enables companies to have an earlier influence on the career choices of the most talented female undergraduates.

Benefit to Employers: Inject fresh thinking into the company and gain the loyalty of undergraduates. Make your company the most sought after within universities by committing fees to a group of cherry-picked talented female students.

● ●

6. Grassroots Employer Brand Campaign.

Bring together the most influential female employees in your organisation and give them a platform to spread company messages. Develop a community that becomes the barometer of how women are feeling in the organisation. Enable them with social media tools and let them be the first ones in the community to know about important issues going on in the organisation. And put an end to those formal inauthentic press releases.

Benefit to Employers: Understand what women really think at all levels of the organisation without having to pay for internal audits and internal focus groups. Use this thinking to drive a mindset shift in the organisation from the ground up.

● ●

7. Tech Skills Requirement Audit.

Are your job-specs over-specific in terms of skill requirements? Research conducted in Australia shows women feel it is important to meet every single criterion an employer desires. Men, by contrast, happily apply with only half the skills an employer lists as desirable.[63] Let's re-focus the job

Men apply with only 50% the skills an employer lists as desirable.[63]

requirements on only the core skills that an employee will need. Let's feature skills which can be acquired 'on the job' as a benefit of the role rather than a barrier to recruitment.

Benefit to Employers: By recruiting from a wider talent pool and not alienating women at the outset, you will have a wider more diverse employee profile.

8. Female Heroes Programme.

Encourage the current women in your company to come forward as external role models. Encourage them to take more prominent positions – give them slots as media commentators and tech pundits. If girls see more female faces talking about tech, they will start to see it as not only acceptable but desirable.

Benefit to Employers: Use women to recruit other women. It's highly effective and will save on recruitment fees.

9. Invest In Female Focused Start-Ups.

Invest in brilliant start-ups such as Roominate – who are using circuit boards to build 'a stackable dollhouse of sorts that gives girls the freedom to design, build, wire, and decorate her own unique interactive room' – and MzTEK – who run workshops where you make interactive and wearable tech – are leading the way in inspiring young girls to be inspired by tech.

Benefit to Employers: Mentor and be part of the early life-stage of these start ups and partner with them and share in their success. Employees will see you as willing to invest in the future and will encourage lateral thinking.

10. Learn To Code In A Day Workshops.

Your next star developer might already be an employee of your company. Your marketing, HR or administration departments might be harbouring untapped talent. Run a programme where your non-technical staff are gradually introduced to the company's core-technologies. Candidates showing particularly high ability should be encouraged to spend days with development teams with a view to gaining a deeper understanding of the company's product.

Benefit to Employers: Widen your talent pool from within the organisation and upskill your staff so they can add more value to your business.

• •

In the time it has taken you to read this sentence the next Little Miss Geek will have been born, somewhere. She will be involved. She will be among the coders, the designers, the inventors and the CEO's. She will be a queen of the industry.

She will be one of these things, because we will not fail her. We will not fail her because we need her. She will help us move forward with the technological revolution. We will be nowhere without her insight, her compassion and her drive. We will be nowhere without her imagination.

Little Miss Geek has arrived.

• •

Lady Geek Performance Index

••

Is your organisation ready to maximise the potential of Female Talent? If you are failing on more than 50% of the questions below, the final chapters will identify practical solutions to help you overcome these issues.

••

1. Engage The Next Generation Of Women

Do you have programmes that reach out to young women in schools and universities?

Do you celebrate the 'Female Heroes' in your organisation and give them a voice both within the industry and externally?

Do your apprenticeship programmes recruit beyond the STEM subjects for technical roles?

2. Recruit Female Talent

Do you research and test job-specs to ensure that they are not off-putting to female applicants?

Does your company have a 'big vision' for why women should work for you?

Does your corporate culture embrace female strengths (e.g. Empathy, Collaboration, and Authenticity)?

Do you have a 'Mum Returner' programme?

Do you conduct exit interviews and split the analysis by gender?

3. Retain Your Female Employees

Do your senior women feel they have to demonstrate male behaviour in order to succeed?

Does your organisation talk openly about gender issues in technology?

Have your staff been trained to understand the common differences between male & female brains (e.g. systemizer vs empathizer)?

Is working for your company seen as being 'glamorous' and 'desirable' externally amongst women?

Have you identified the most common reasons that might influence women to leave your company?

4. Promote Your Female Talent To The Boardroom

Do you empower your staff to promote women?

Is your board of directors more than 25% female?

Do women in your organisation have internal sponsors or mentors?

Do female employees have a clear career progression path?

5. Market Your Products Successfully To Female Consumers

Are women in your ads empowered by technology?

Do you avoid using stereotypes in your advertising (i.e. pink tech as a fashion accessory)?

Do you have an in-depth understanding of the women you are speaking to i.e. beyond a segment definition?

What proportion of your product managers are female?

Endnotes

[1] E-Skills. (2011). Analysis of data from the ONS Labour Force Survey 2001 to 2010. London: Author.

[2] Lady Geek (2010). Why You Need To Speak To Women. Ladygeek.org.uk. Retrieved July 12, 2012, from http://ladygeek.com/facts/.

[3] Prescott, J. & Bogg, J. (2011). Segregation in a Male-Dominated Industry: Women Working in the Computer Games Industry. International Journal of Gender, Science and Technology, 3(1), 205-267.

[4] Lady Geek. (2011). Just Who Is The Casual Female Gamer?. London: Author.

[5] E-Skills. (2011). Analysis of data from the ONS Labour Force Survey 2001 to 2010. London: Author.

[6] TP-Link. (2011). Connectivity Report. UK: Author.

[7] Vertis Communications. (2008). Consumer Focus Study. Baltimore: Author.

[8] E-Skills. (2011). Analysis of Joint Council for Qualifications results 2004-2011. London: Author.

[9] NCWIT. (2009). Women in IT: The Facts. Colorado: University of Colorado.

[10] NCWIT. (2009). Women in IT: The Facts. Colorado: University of Colorado.

[11] E-Skills. (2011). Analysis of Joint Council for Qualifications results 2004-2011. London: Author.

[12] Catalyst. (2004). The Bottom Line: Connecting Corporate Performance and Gender Diversity. New York: Author.

[13] Silverstein, M.J. and Sayre, K. (2009). The Female Economy. Harvard Business Review, September 2009. Boston, MA: Harvard Business Publishing.

[14] Debry, M., Gras-Velazquez, A. & Joyce, A. (2009). Women and ICT: Why are girls still not attracted to ICT studies and careers?. Brussels: European Schoolnet.

[15] Debry, M., Gras-Velazquez, A. & Joyce, A. (2009). Women and ICT: Why are girls still not attracted to ICT studies and careers?. Brussels: European Schoolnet.

[16] Fisher, A. & Margolis, J. (2003). Unlocking the Clubhouse: Women in Computing. Cambridge, MA: MIT Press.

[17] Goudreau, J. (2011). The Best-Paying Jobs For Women in 2011. Forbes. Retrieved 14 July, 2012, from http://www.forbes.com/sites/jennagoudreau/2011/04/20/best-paying-jobs-for-women-2011/.

[18] Baron-Cohen, S. (2004). The Essential Difference. London: Penguin.

[19] Baron-Cohen, S. (2004). The Essential Difference. London: Penguin.

[20] Grossi, G. & Nash, A. (2007). Picking Barbie's Brain: Inherent Sex Differences in Scientific Ability?. Journal of Interdisciplinary Feminist Thought, 2(1).

[21] New York Times. (1992). Mattel Says It Erred; Teen Talk Barbie Turns Silent on Math. New York Times. Retrieved July 11, 2012, from http://www.nytimes.com/1992/10/21/business/company-news-mattel-says-it-erred-teen-talk-barbie-turns-silent-on-math.html?scp=1.

[22] Corbett, C., Hill, C. & St. Rose, A. (2010). Why So Few? Women in Science, Technology, Engineering, and Mathematics. Washington, DC: AAUW.

[23] Steele, C.M. & Aronson, J. (1995). Stereotype threat and the intellectual test-performance of African Americans. Journal of Personality and Social Psychology, 69 (5), 797-811.

[24] Corbett, C., Hill, C. & St. Rose, A. (2010). Why So Few? Women in Science, Technology, Engineering, and Mathematics. Washington, DC: AAUW.

[25] Norman, K.L. (1994). Spatial Visualization – A gateway to computer-based technology. Journal of Special Educational Technology, 12(3), 195-206.

[26] Baartmans, B.J. & Sorby, S.A. (2000). The Development and Assessment of a Course for Enhancing the 3-D Spatial Visualization Skills of First Year Engineering Students. Journal of Engineering Education, 89(3), 301-307.

[27] Sorby, S.A. (2001). A Course In Spatial Visualization and its Impact on the Retention of Female Engineering Students. Journal of Women and Minorities in Science and Engineering, 7, 153-172.

[28] Sorby, S. A., Leopold, C., & Gorska, R. (1999). Cross-cultural comparisons of gender

[29] University Of Toronto. (2007). Playing Video Games Reduces Sex Differences In Spatial Skills. Science Daily. Retrieved July 11, 2012, from http://www.sciencedaily.com≠ /releases/2007/10/071024145626.htm.

[30] Schwab, S. (2012). Girl LEGOs' Betray Imagination. The Observer, NY. Retrieved July 11, 2012, from http://www.observertoday.com/page/content.detail/id/567093/Girl-LEGOs--betray-imagination.html?nav=5046.

[31] WGBH Educational Foundation & Association for Computing Machinery. (2009). Report on Market Research. Boston, MA: Author.

[32] Debry, M., Gras-Velazquez, A. & Joyce, A. (2009). Women and ICT: Why are girls still not attracted to ICT studies and careers?. Brussels: European Schoolnet.

[33] European Centre for Women and Technology. (2008). Women in ICT: Status and the way ahead. Drammen, Norway: Author.

[34] Debry, M., Gras-Velazquez, A. & Joyce, A. (2009). Women and ICT: Why are girls still not attracted to ICT studies and careers?. Brussels: European Schoolnet.

[35] Debry, M., Gras-Velazquez, A. & Joyce, A. (2009). Women and ICT: Why are girls still not attracted to ICT studies and careers?. Brussels: European Schoolnet.

[36] Hormby, T. (2007). Acorn and the BBC Micro: From Education to Obscurity. Low End Mac. Retrieved 11 July, 2012 from http://lowendmac.com/orchard/07/0228.html

[37] BBC (2011). The BBC Microcomputer and me, 30 years down the line. BBC News Technology. Retrieved 11 July, 2012, from http://www.bbc.co.uk/news/technology-15969065.

[38] E-Skills. (2011). Analysis of Joint Council for Qualifications results 2004-2011. London: Author.

[39] E-Skills. (2011). Analysis of Joint Council for Qualifications results 2004-2011. London: Author.

[40] E-Skills. (2011). Analysis of Joint Council for Qualifications results 2004-2011. London: Author.

[41] Young Rewired State. (2012). Who is Rewired State?. Young Rewired State, Retrieved July 13th, 2012, from http://youngrewiredstate.org/.

[42] Gove, M. (2012). Speech at the BETT Show 2012. Department for Education. Retrieved 14th June, 2012, from http://www.education.gov.uk/inthenews/speeches/a00201868/michael-gove-speech-at-the-bett-show-2012.

[43] Livingstone, I. & Hope, A. (2011). Next Gen. UK: NESTA.

[44] Raspberry Pi (2012). About Us. Raspberry Pi. Retrieved on July 13th, 2012 from www.raspberrypi.org

[45] Schmidt, E. (2011). MacTaggart Lecture 2011. Guardian Media. Retrieved July 13th, 2012, from http://www.guardian.co.uk/media/interactive/2011/aug/26/eric-schmidt-mactaggart-lecture-full-text.

[46] ASUS (@ASUS) (2012). "The rear looks pretty nice. So does the new Transformer AIO." 4th June, 2012.

[47] Simard, C. (2007). Barriers to the Advancement of Technical Women – A Review of the Literature Palo Alto, CA: Anita Borg Institute.

[48] Women in Technology. (2011). Women's Careers in the Technology Industry. London: Intellect.

[49] Women in Technology. (2011). Women's Careers in the Technology Industry. London: Intellect.

[50] Simard, C. (2007). Barriers to the Advancement of Technical Women – A Review of the Literature. Palo Alto, CA: Anita Borg Institute.

[51] Baron-Cohen, S. (2004). The Essential Difference. London: Penguin.

[52] Women in Technology. (2011). Women's Careers in the Technology Industry. London: Intellect.

[53] O'Leonard, K. (2011). U.K. Talent Acquisition Factbook 2011: Benchmarks and Trends in Spending, Staffing and Key Recruiting Metrics. London: Bersin and Associates.

[54] Parmar, B. (2012) Why a Woman's Femininity is her Strength. Huffington Post. Retrieved on 11 July, 2012 from http://www.huffingtonpost.co.uk/belinda-parmar/women-in-tech-why-a-womans-femininity-i_b_1520732.html

[55] Foust-Cummings, H., Sabattini, L. & Carter, N. (2008). Women In Technology – Maximising Talent, Minimizing Barriers. New York: Catalyst.

[56] Barbian, J. (1999). The Road Best Travelled. Training, May 2002 or Retention and Staffing Report. Manchester: Manchester Inc.

[57] Alleman, E. and Clarke, D.L. Accountability: Measuring Mentoring and Its Bottom Line Impact. Review of Business, March 22, 2000.

[58] Women in Technology (2011). Women's Careers in the Technology Industry. London: Intellect.

[59] Foust-Cummings, H., Sabattini, L. & Carter, N. (2008). Women In Technology – Maximising Talent, Minimizing Barriers. New York: Catalyst.

[60] Simard, C. (2007). Barriers to the Advancement of Technical Women – A Review of the Literature. Palo Alto, CA: Anita Borg Institute.

[61] NCWIT. (2009). Women in IT: The Facts. Colorado: University of Colorado.

[62] Pande, R. & Ford, D. (2011). Gender, Quotas and Female Leadership. World Development Report 2012: Gender Equality and Development.

[63] Sharwood, S. (2012). Why women won't apply for IT jobs. The Register. Retrieved July 21, 2012 from http://www.theregister.co.uk/2012/08/07/women_wont_apply_for_it_jobs/.

Bibliography

Alleman, E. & Clarke, D.L. (2000). Accountability: Measuring Mentoring and Its Bottom Line Impact. Review of Business, March 22, 2000.

Baartmans, B.J. & Sorby, S.A. (1996). A Course for the Development of 3-D Spatial Visualisation Skills. Engineering Design Graphics Journal, Winter 1996, 13-20.

Baartmans, B.J. & Sorby, S.A. (2000). The Development and Assessment of a Course for Enhancing the 3-D Spatial Visualization Skills of First Year Engineering Students. Journal of Engineering Education, 89(3), 301-307.

Barbian, J. (1999). The Road Best Travelled. Training, May 2002 or Retention and Staffing Report. Manchester: Manchester Inc.

Baron-Cohen, S. (2004). The Essential Difference. London: Penguin.

Camp, T. (2001). Women in Computer Sciences: Reversing the Trend. Syllabus, August 2001, 24-26.

Catalyst. (2004). The Bottom Line: Connecting Corporate Performance and Gender Diversity. New York: Author.

Corbett, C., Hill, C. & St. Rose, A. (2010). Why So Few? Women in Science, Technology, Engineering, and Mathematics. Washington, DC: AAUW.

Debry, M., Gras-Velazquez, A. & Joyce, A. (2009). Women and ICT: Why are girls still not attracted to ICT studies and careers?. Brussels: European Schoolnet.

Dweck, C. (2006). Is math a gift? Beliefs that put females at risk. In S.J. Ceci & W.M. Williams (Eds.), Why Aren't More Women in Science? Top Researchers Debate the Evidence. (pp. 47-55). Washington, DC: American Psychological Association.

E-Skills. (2011). Analysis of data from the ONS Labour Force Survey 2001 to 2010. London: Author.

E-Skills. (2011). Analysis of Joint Council for Qualifications results 2004-2011. London: Author.

European Centre for Women and Technology. (2008). Women in ICT: Status and the way ahead. Drammen, Norway: Author.

Fisher, A. & Margolis, J. (2003). Unlocking the Clubhouse: Women in Computing. Cambridge, MA: MIT Press.

Foust-Cummings, H., Sabattini, L. & Carter, N. (2008). Women In Technology – Maximizing Talent, Minimizing Barriers. New York: Catalyst.

Goudreau, J. (2011). The Best-Paying Jobs For Women in 2011. Forbes. Retrieved 14 July, 2012, from http://www.forbes.com/sites/jennagoudreau/2011/04/20/best-paying-jobs-for-women-2011/.

Gove, M. (2012). Speech at the BETT Show 2012. Department for Education. Retrieved 14th June, 2012, from http://www.education.gov.uk/inthenews/speeches/a00201868/michael-gove-speech-at-the-bett-show-2012.

Grossi, G. & Nash, A. (2007). Picking Barbie's Brain: Inherent Sex Differences in Scientific Ability?. Journal of Interdisciplinary Feminist Thought, 2(1).

Johns, M., Schmader, T., & Martens, A. (2005). Knowing is half the battle: Teaching stereotype threat as a means of improving women's math performance. Psychological Science, 16(3), 175-79.

Livingstone, I. & Hope, A. (2011). Next Gen. UK: NESTA.

Margolis, J., Fisher, A., & Miller, F. (2002). Caring about connections: Gender and computing. Pittsburgh, PA: Carnegie Mellon University, School of Computer Science.

McCorduck, P. & Ramsey, N. (2005). Where are the Women in Information Technology?. Colorado: University of Colorado.

NCWIT. (2007). NCWIT Scorecard 2007. Colorado: University of Colorado.

NCWIT. (2009). Women in IT: The Facts. Colorado: University of Colorado.

New York Times. (1992). Mattel Says It Erred; Teen Talk Barbie Turns Silent on Math. New York Times. Retrieved July 11, 2012, from http://www.nytimes.com/1992/10/21/business/company-news-mattel-says-it-erred-teen-talk-barbie-turns-silent-on-math.html?scp=1.

Norman, K.L. (1994). Spatial Visualization – A gateway to computer-based technology. Journal of Special Educational Technology, 12(3), 195-206.

O'Leonard, K. (2011). U.K. Talent Acquisition Factbook 2011: Benchmarks and Trends in Spending, Staffing and Key Recruiting Metrics. London: Bersin and Associates.

Schmidt, E. (2011). MacTaggart Lecture 2011. Guardian Media. Retrieved July 13th, 2012, from http://www.guardian.co.uk/media/interactive/2011/aug/26/eric-schmidt-mactaggart-lecture-full-text.

Schwab, S. (2012). Girl LEGOs' Betray Imagination. The Observer, NY. Retrieved July 11, 2012, from http://www.observertoday.com/page/content.detail/id/567093/Girl-LEGOs--betray-imagination.html?nav=5046.

Silverstein, M.J. and Sayre, K. (2009). The Female Economy. Harvard Business Review, September 2009. Boston, MA: Harvard Business Publishing.

Simard, C. (2007). Barriers to the Advancement of Technical Women – A Review of the Literature. Palo Alto, CA: Anita Borg Institute.

Sorby, S. A., Leopold, C., & Gorska, R. (1999). Cross-cultural comparisons of gender differences in the spatial skills of engineering students. Journal of Women and Minorities in Science and Engineering, 5, 279-291.

Sorby, S.A. (2001). A Course In Spatial Visualization and its Impact on the Retention of Female Engineering Students. Journal of Women and Minorities in Science and Engineering, 7, 153-172.

Steele, C.M. & Aronson, J. (1995). Stereotype threat and the intellectual test-performance of African Americans. Journal of Personality and Social Psychology, 69 (5), 797-811.

Steele, C.M. (1997). A threat in the air. How stereotypes shape intellectual identity and performance. American Psychologist, 52(6), 613-29.

TP-Link. (2011). Connectivity Report. UK: Author.

University Of Toronto. (2007). Playing Video Games Reduces Sex Differences In Spatial Skills. ScienceDaily. Retrieved July 11, 2012, from http://www.sciencedaily.com≠ /releases/2007/10/0710 24145626.htm.

Vertis Communications. (2008). Consumer Focus Study. Baltimore: Author.

WGBH Educational Foundation & Association for Computing Machinery. (2009). Report on Market Research. Boston, MA: Author.

Women in Technology. (2011). Women's Careers in the Technology Industry. London: Intellect.

Young Rewired State. (2012). Who is Rewired State?. Young Rewired State, Retrieved July 13th, 2012, from http://youngrewiredstate.org/.